PERIODIC TABLE

1																	2
H 1.008																	**He** 4.00
3 **Li** 6.94	4 **Be** 9.01											5 **B** 10.8	6 **C** 12.01	7 **N** 14.01	8 **O** 16.00	9 **F** 19.0	10 **Ne** 20.2
11 **Na** 23.0	12 **Mg** 24.3											13 **Al** 27.0	14 **Si** 28.1	15 **P** 31.0	16 **S** 32.1	17 **Cl** 35.5	18 **Ar** 39.9
19 **K** 39.1	20 **Ca** 40.1	21 **Sc** 45.0	22 **Ti** 47.9	23 **V** 50.9	24 **Cr** 52.0	25 **Mn** 54.9	26 **Fe** 55.8	27 **Co** 58.9	28 **Ni** 58.7	29 **Cu** 63.5	30 **Zn** 65.4	31 **Ga** 69.7	32 **Ge** 72.6	33 **As** 74.9	34 **Se** 79.0	35 **Br** 79.9	36 **Kr** 83.8
37 **Rb** 85.5	38 **Sr** 87.6	39 **Y** 88.9	40 **Zr** 91.2	41 **Nb** 92.9	42 **Mo** 95.9	43 **Tc** (99)	44 **Ru** 101.1	45 **Rh** 102.9	46 **Pd** 106.4	47 **Ag** 107.9	48 **Cd** 112.4	49 **In** 114.8	50 **Sn** 118.7	51 **Sb** 121.8	52 **Te** 127.6	53 **I** 126.9	54 **Xe** 131.3
55 **Cs** 132.9	56 **Ba** 137.3	57–71 See below	72 **Hf** 178.5	73 **Ta** 180.9	74 **W** 183.9	75 **Re** 186.2	76 **Os** 190.2	77 **Ir** 192.2	78 **Pt** 195.1	79 **Au** 197.0	80 **Hg** 200.6	81 **Tl** 204.4	82 **Pb** 207.2	83 **Bi** 209.0	84 **Po** (209)	85 **At** (210)	86 **Rn** (222)
87 **Fr** (223)	88 **Ra** (226)	89– See below															

57 **La** 138.9	58 **Ce** 140.1	59 **Pr** 140.9	60 **Nd** 144.2	61 **Pm** (147)	62 **Sm** 150.4	63 **Eu** 152.0	64 **Gd** 157.3	65 **Tb** 158.9	66 **Dy** 162.5	67 **Ho** 164.9	68 **Er** 167.3	69 **Tm** 168.9	70 **Yb** 173.0	71 **Lu** 175.0
89 **Ac** (227)	90 **Th** 232.0	91 **Pa** (231)	92 **U** 238.0	93 **Np** (237)	94 **Pu** (242)	95 **Am** (243)	96 **Cm** (247)	97 **Bk** (245)	98 **Cf** (251)	99 **Es** (254)	100 **Fm** (253)	101 **Md** (256)	102 **No** (254)	103 **Lw** (257)

Parenthetical values are mass numbers of the isotopes with longest half lives

LABORATORY MANUAL FOR

CHEMISTRY

AN EXPERIMENTAL SCIENCE

Laboratory Manual for

CHEMISTRY

Prepared by

CHEMICAL EDUCATION MATERIAL STUDY

Under a grant from

THE NATIONAL SCIENCE FOUNDATION

Editor: LLOYD E. MALM, University of Utah, Salt Lake City, Utah

Associate Editors
JOSEPH E. DAVIS, JR., Miramonte High School, Orinda, California

MARGARET NICHOLSON, Acalanes High School, Lafayette, California

An Experimental Science

Contributors

ROBERT F. CAMPBELL
Miramonte High School, Orinda, California

SAUL L. GEFFNER
Forest Hills High School, Forest Hills, New York

THEODORE A. GEISSMAN
University of California, Los Angeles, California

MELVIN GREENSTADT
Fairfax High School, Los Angeles, California

CARL GRUHN
South Pasadena High School, South Pasadena, California

EDWARD L. HAENISCH
Wabash College, Crawfordsville, Indiana

ROLFE H. HERBER
Rutgers University, New Brunswick, New Jersey

C. ROBERT HURLEY
Sacramento State College, Sacramento, California

LAWRENCE D. LYNCH, JR.
Beverly Hills High School, Beverly Hills, California

KEITH MacNAB
Sir Francis Drake High School, San Anselmo, California

BRUCE H. MAHAN
University of California, Berkeley, California

A. L. McCLELLAN
California Research Corporation, Richmond, California

CLYDE E. PARRISH
Cubberley Senior High School, Palo Alto, California

ROBERT W. PARRY
University of Michigan, Ann Arbor, Michigan

GEORGE C. PIMENTEL
University of California, Berkeley, California

EUGENE ROBERTS
Polytechnic High School, San Francisco, California

MICHELL J. SIENKO
Cornell University, Ithaca, New York

ROBERT SILBER
American Chemical Society, Washington, D.C.

HARLEY L. SORENSEN
San Ramon Valley Union High School, Danville, California

LUKE E. STEINER
Oberlin College, Oberlin, Ohio

MODDIE D. TAYLOR
Howard University, Washington, D.C.

ROBERT L. TELLEFSEN
Napa High School, Napa, California

Director: J. ARTHUR CAMPBELL Harvey Mudd College, Claremont, California

Chairman: GLENN T. SEABORG University of California, Berkeley, California

W. H. FREEMAN AND COMPANY, *Cooperating Publishers*

SAN FRANCISCO AND LONDON

First printing 1963
Second printing 1963
Third printing 1964
Fourth printing 1965
Fifth printing 1965

Sixth printing 1966

Seventh printing 1966

Eighth printing 1967

Ninth Printing 1968

Printed in the United States of America.   (B9)

PREFACE

The CHEM Study course approaches the study of chemistry as an experimental science. It is a *laboratory-centered* course which:

(1) features experiments which will permit you to make your own discoveries of the regularities and principles which unify chemistry and make it easier to understand,

(2) emphasizes the making of careful observations and quantitative measurements under controlled experimental conditions,

(3) stresses the preparation of well-organized tables for recording data and the results of calculations so that you can more readily make deductions and recognize the regularities which exist,

(4) uses challenging discussion questions which will help you to apply the principles observed in the experiments to new situations.

The Textbook discussions are closely meshed with the laboratory work. Each chapter in the Textbook is preceded by one or more experiments which provide an experimental background for the topics discussed. As you learn to recognize and use the important principles you will be in a better position to appreciate and understand the theories which have been proposed to explain the regularities in chemistry.

The organization of the CHEM Study course is revealed by the five major divisions into which the experiments have been classified:

Part I. Observation and Interpretation. Precision of Measurement. (Six experiments)

Part II. An Introduction to Chemistry. The Mole Concept. Avogadro's Hypothesis. Gases. Solutions. (Eight experiments)

Part III. Investigations of Chemical Reactions Illustrating Important Principles. (Thirteen experiments)

Part IV. Theoretical Concepts. Atomic Structure. Chemical Bonds. Structure and Properties. (Four experiments)

Part V. Application of Chemical Principles to Descriptive Chemistry. (Fifteen experiments)

Familiarize yourself with each experiment you are to perform before coming to the laboratory. Prepare tables for recording data and calculations in a blank laboratory notebook. Read carefully the directions on page ix for writing laboratory reports. The introductory section of the manual contains two full page illustrations of laboratory apparatus you will use. Read carefully the laboratory instructions and safety precautions on page ix.

Gain self-reliance by working alone on an experiment unless directed otherwise. Use your ingenuity and common sense. You will find that there is always opportunity for logical and imaginative thinking.

Illustrated sections on lighting and adjusting a laboratory burner and manipulating glass tubing will be found in Appendixes 1 and 2. Appendixes 3, 4, and 5 deal with the metric system, experimental errors, and a brief review of some mathematics which will be useful to you in making calculations. Appendix 6 contains additional experiments which you may perform at the option of your teacher. Many experiments contain suggestions for additional investigations which may be undertaken with the permission of your teacher.

Remember that your laboratory work is the

core of your chemistry course. You have a unique and challenging opportunity to observe first-hand many of the facts and regularities of chemistry. Out of such observations scientists developed the principles that unify chemistry and the theories which provide the current explanations. This is the scientific method in action.

The teachers and students who used the three trial editions of this manual have made important contributions to this edition. Because of their valuable suggestions and their participation in many evaluation sessions, we were provided with a reliable basis for the revision presented here. All members of the CHEM Study staff have contributed to the development of the experiments.

In particular we wish to acknowledge the significant contributions made by the following high school teachers on our staff: Mr. Joseph E. Davis, Miramonte High School, Orinda, California, Mr. Keith MacNab, Sir Francis Drake High School, San Anselmo, California, and Miss Margaret Nicholson, Acalanes High School, Lafayette, California.

There are numberless ways in which the CHEM Study is indebted to the institutions listed below for contributions of personnel, facilities, and encouragement. Finally, we acknowledge with thanks the stimulation and support received from the National Science Foundation that made the CHEM Study possible.

January 1963

LLOYD E. MALM,
Editor, *Laboratory Manual*
University of Utah

GEORGE C. PIMENTEL,
Editor, *Textbook*
University of California

A. L. MCCLELLAN,
Editor, *Teachers Guide*
California Research Corporation

J. ARTHUR CAMPBELL,
Director, Chemical Education Material Study
Harvey Mudd College

CONTENTS

LABORATORY INSTRUCTIONS

1. Remember at all times that the laboratory is a place for serious work.
2. Always prepare for an experiment by reading the directions in the manual before you come to the lab. Follow the directions implicitly and intelligently, noting carefully all precautions. Check any deviations contemplated with your teacher.
3. **Do only the experiments assigned or approved by your teacher. Unauthorized experiments are prohibited.**
4. If an acid or other corrosive chemical is spilled, wash it off immediately with water.
5. Do not touch chemicals with your hands unless directed to do so.
6. Never taste a chemical or solution unless directed to do so.
7. When observing the odor of a substance, do not hold your face directly over the container. Fan a little of the vapor toward you by sweeping your hand over the top of the container.
8. Allow ample time for hot glass to cool. Remember hot glass *looks* like cool glass.
9. Smother any fires with a towel. Also, be sure you know the location of the fire extinguisher in the laboratory.
10. **Report any accident, even a minor injury, to your teacher.**
11. Wear protective eye goggles when handling dangerous chemicals. Use the fume hood when directed.
12. Throw all solids and paper to be discarded into a waste jar or waste basket. Never discard matches, filter paper, or any slightly soluble solids, in the sink.
13. Check the label on a reagent bottle carefully before removing any of its contents. Read the label twice to be sure you have the right bottle.
14. Never return unused chemicals to the stock bottles. Do not put any object into a reagent bottle except the dropper with which it may be equipped.
15. Keep your apparatus and desk top clean. Avoid spillage, but if you do spill something, clean it up immediately. Put your own equipment into your drawer and return any special apparatus to its proper place at the end of the period.

LABORATORY REPORTS

1. Record all data in a laboratory notebook as soon as possible after making the observations. Make no erasures; instead, cross out any errors with a single line. Always record your name, the date, and the title of the experiment.
2. Enter all data and observations neatly. Use tabular form whenever it is appropriate. When possible, design a data table before coming to the laboratory.
3. Indicate the operations used in making calculations by showing an orderly sample calculation. Do not clutter the calculations section with arithmetic details. Indicate the units used for all measurements. Normally calculations should not be made during the laboratory period.
4. *Answer the numbered questions* wherever they appear as part of your laboratory report. Use concise statements.
5. *Do not include written answers* to questions which appear in the introduction and procedure section. Some are intended to direct your attention to problems which will be investigated. Others point out the reason for certain procedures or controls which will enable you to proceed with greater understanding.

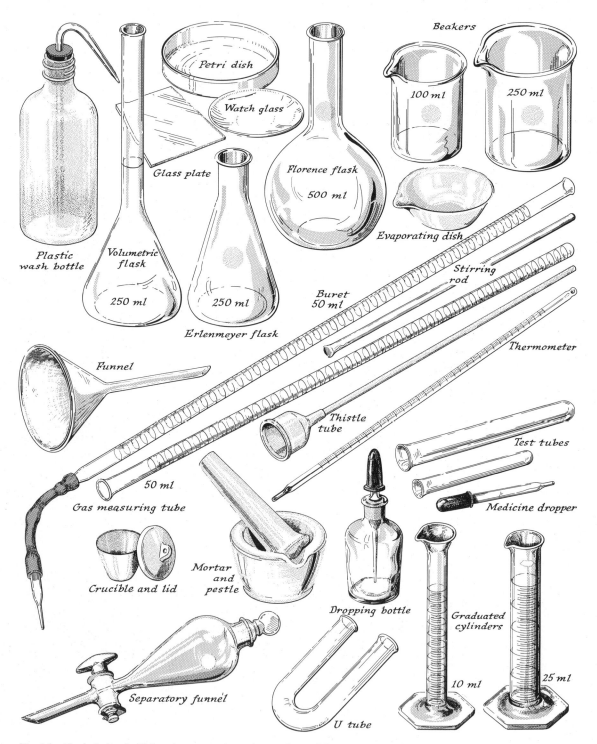

Fig. i-1. Typical chemical laboratory apparatus—*glass and porcelain.*

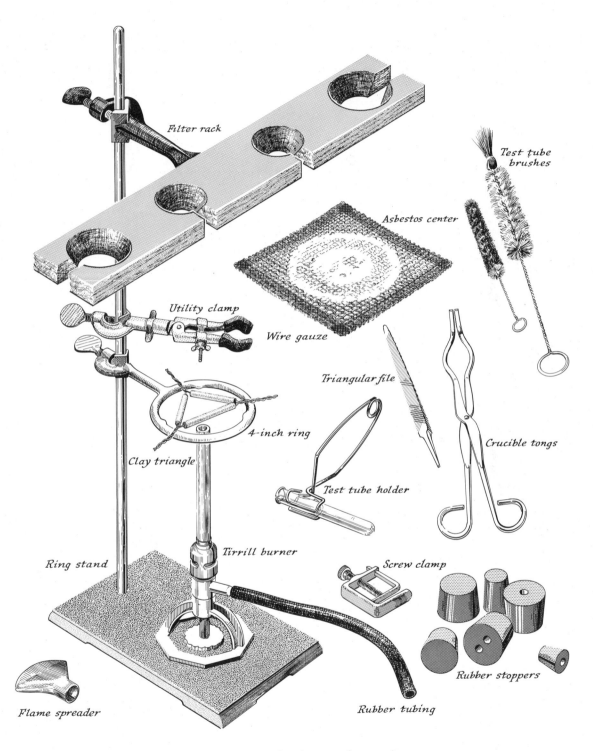

Filter rack

Test tube brushes

Asbestos center

Utility clamp

Wire gauze

Triangular file

4-inch ring

Crucible tongs

Clay triangle

Test tube holder

Ring stand

Tirrill burner

Screw clamp

Flame spreader

Rubber stoppers

Rubber tubing

Fig. i-2. Typical chemical laboratory apparatus — *metal equipment and accessories.*

SCIENTIFIC OBSERVATION AND DESCRIPTION

Everyone thinks of himself as a good observer. Yet there is much more to observation than meets the eye. It takes concentration, alertness to detail, ingenuity, and often just plain patience. It even takes practice! Try it yourself. See how complete a description you can write about a familiar object—say, a burning candle. Be "scientific" about this and start with an experiment. This means you should observe a burning candle in a laboratory, that is, a place where conditions can be controlled. But how do we know what conditions need be controlled? Be ready for surprises here! Sometimes the important conditions are difficult to discover but an experiment can be meaningless unless the *conditions that matter* are controlled. Here are some conditions that may be important in *some* experiments but are not important here.

The experiment is done on the second floor.
The experiment is done in the daytime.
The room lights are on.

Here are some conditions that *might* be important in your experiment.

The lab bench is near the door.
The windows are open.
You are standing close enough to the candle to breathe on it.

Why are these conditions important? Do they have something in common? Yes, there is the common factor that a candle does not operate well in a draft. Important conditions are often not as easily recognized as these. A good experimentalist pays much attention to the discovery and control of conditions that are important.

PROCEDURE

First examine the candle carefully. Then light it, and record in your notebook as many observations as you can during a short period (10–15 minutes).

Turn in the carbon copy of your observations to your teacher before you leave the laboratory.

Write a description of a burning candle, based upon your list of observations and upon any additional observations of burning candles you care to make later at home.

2

BEHAVIOR OF SOLIDS
ON WARMING

Careful observation of a familiar object usually reveals characteristics not recognized before. You noted this as you studied the candle in Experiment 1. These details of observation raise questions. Let us give attention to one such question:

"What is the colorless liquid in the bowl at the top of the burning candle?"

This is a question with a ready answer. Perhaps the liquid is just melted wax. But how do you know this? What evidence can you offer? What kind of experiment would help you to decide if this ready answer is correct?

Let us proceed by comparing the behavior of several different substances when heated.

PROCEDURE

Part I

a. Place a tin can lid, tinned side up, on an iron ring attached to a ring stand as shown in Fig. 2-1. The lid should have three depressions to contain some of the substances tested—see (b). Adjust the height of the ring until the lid is about 8 centimeters (cm) above the candle (1 cm is almost ½ inch).

b. Place on the lid, equally spaced near the edge, small, approximately equal amounts of each of the following substances (a quantity about the size of a match head is appropriate):

candle wax	lead
steel wool	tin
sulfur	copper wire
silver chloride	

Place the candle wax, sulfur, and silver chloride each in a separate depression in the lid, and space the other substances as shown in Fig. 2-1. The amount and location on the lid are *conditions that matter*.

c. Light the candle, and adjust the ring height until the tip of the flame is about 4 cm directly below the center of the lid. Heat the lid for about 3 minutes. Record your observations as you make them, paying particular attention to the melting behavior.

Fig. 2-1. **Arrangement of substances on a lid.**

d. Remove the candle and adjust the height of the iron ring so the lid is about 8 cm above the top of a burner. (See Appendix 1 for directions for lighting and adjusting the burner.) Heat the lid with the burner flame adjusted about 5 cm high for about 3 minutes. Increase the size of the flame and heat for several minutes more. Record your observations.

Part II

Now let us heat some of the solidified liquid from the bowl of the candle and some of the candle wax to see how they compare.

a. Remove the lid from the ring stand and replace it with a wire gauze and a 250 milliliter (ml) beaker or small tin can about one-third full of water. See Fig. 2-2.
b. Pour a few drops of the liquid from the bowl of a burning candle onto a piece of paper. Break off a small piece of the solid and place it on the water contained in the beaker or can. Obtain a piece of candle wax by cutting a chip from the bottom of your candle. Both pieces should be about the same size. Place the second piece on the water in the beaker or can apart from the first piece.
c. Heat the beaker or can and its contents with a burner flame and note when each substance starts to melt. Allow the wax to solidify, then discard it in the waste jar. *Do not pour liquid wax into the sink.*

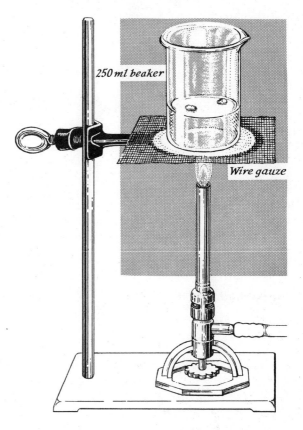

Fig. 2-2. **Comparing melting behavior.**

QUESTIONS AND EXERCISES

1. How does your observed order of melting for the substances tested compare with that observed by other members of the class?

2. Make a generalization based on the combined observations.

3. What statement can you make concerning the material in the bowl of the burning candle and the candle wax, based upon your generalization from Exercise 2?

A Question to Wonder About

Why did the substances tested on the lid begin to melt at different temperatures?

3

THE MELTING TEMPERATURE
OF A PURE SUBSTANCE

The method used in Experiment 2 to determine the order in which materials melt as the temperature is raised is a satisfactory experimental technique but not a convenient one. Chemical stockrooms contain several hundred different chemicals and if we were to follow this method, we would have to place each on the lid. A more practical method is to measure separately the temperature of melting (the melting point) of each of the substances. Then these characteristic temperatures can be filed for comparison with the measured melting points of any other sample

at any later time.

Until now we have been dealing only with the relative order of melting points. Now let us look at the melting of one substance more closely. A solid, *para*dichlorobenzene, will be heated slightly above its melting temperature. Temperature data will be obtained by noting the temperature at designated time intervals as the liquid cools and solidifies. The solid will then be reheated and melted, and again temperature data will be obtained at designated time intervals during the heating.

PROCEDURE

Part I. Cooling Behavior

a. To facilitate the recording of data in this experiment, you should work with a partner. One partner should prepare a table in his notebook which will allow him to record systematically the temperature, the time, and the cooling behavior. Two additional copies of the data should be made—one will be handed in; one is for the other partner (that is, there should be two copies and one original). See the sample data table at the end of this experiment.

b. Fill a 400 ml beaker three-fourths full of tap water at about room temperature (below 30°C). Place the beaker on the base of your ring stand.

c. Slowly raise the temperature of about 15 grams (g) of the moth repellant *para*dichlorobenzene in a test tube until it melts. Heat the test tube with the burner adjusted to a low flame. Place a thermometer in the liquid and continue heating until the temperature is between 65°C and 70°C. Continuously move the test tube back and forth through the flame as shown in Fig. 3-1.

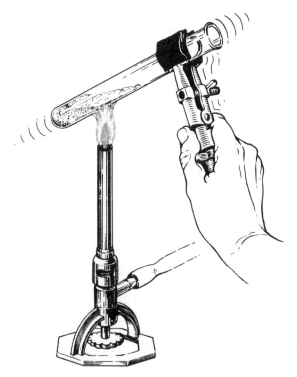

Fig. 3-1. **Melting the solid crystals.**

d. Clamp the test tube containing the melted *para*dichlorobenzene into position above the beaker of water.

e. Now clearly divide your labor. Place a clock or watch in such a way that one partner, the recorder, can read the time every 30 seconds. This partner also is to record all the observations noted by the other partner.

f. When all is ready, check the temperature of the *para*dichlorobenzene and record it to the nearest 0.2°C. On signal by the recorder, immediately immerse the lower half of the test tube into the water bath and clamp the test tube in position. Hold the thermometer against the side and just off the bottom of the

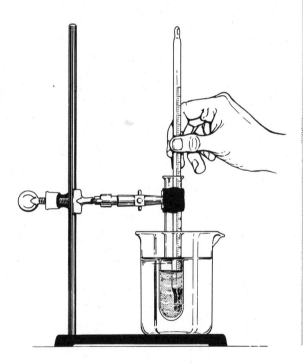

Fig. 3-2. **Apparatus for observing the cooling behavior.**

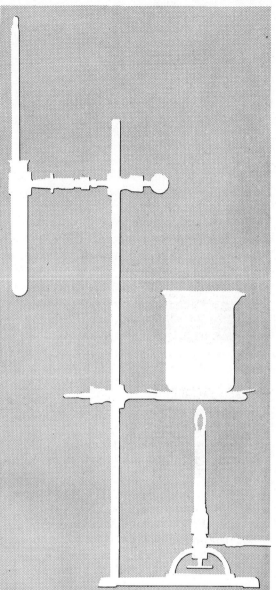

Fig. 3-3. **Apparatus for observing the warming behavior.**

test tube so that it will become imbedded in that position when the *para*dichlorobenzene solidifies (see Fig. 3-2). Record the temperature each 30 seconds until a temperature in the upper thirties is reached. Note also when solidification starts and when it is complete.

Part II. Warming Behavior

The observer and recorder should exchange duties at this point.

a. Raise the test tube out of the water bath and turn the clamp around so the test tube is on the other side of the ring stand, opposite the water bath, as shown in Fig. 3-3. Place the beaker, three-fourths full of water, on an iron ring and wire gauze. Heat the water bath to approximately 70°C (start with hot tap water, if available, to save heating time), then turn off the burner, but leave it in position.

b. Record the temperature of the solidified *para*dichlorobenzene to the nearest 0.2°C. With a second thermometer measure the temperature of the hot water bath to the nearest 1°C. On signal by the recorder, immerse the lower half of the test tube into the water bath until the water level is above the level of the *para*-dichlorobenzene. Record the temperature of the *para*dichlorobenzene each 30 seconds, noting when melting starts and completes.

c. As soon as the solid becomes free from the walls of the test tube, move the thermometer gently up and down. Occasionally note the temperature of the water bath with the second thermometer. If the water temperature drops below 60°C before the solid is melted, be prepared to warm it with the burner flame to keep the temperature between 60°C and 65°C. Continue to move the thermometer up and down in the test tube and to record temperatures until the temperature of the *para*dichlorobenzene is about 60°C.

Sample Table for Data

The following type of table should be reproduced in your notebook and used for recording the data obtained on cooling; a similar table should be made for the data obtained on heating.

Time	Temperature (°C)	Observations and Remarks
0 seconds		
30 seconds		
1 minute		
etc.		
Continue to about 8 minutes		

QUESTIONS

1. What effect would increasing the amount of *para*-dichlorobenzene have on the shape of the melting or cooling curves?

2. Based on your data, what is the melting temperature of the *para*dichlorobenzene?

3. Based on your data, what is the freezing temperature of the *para*dichlorobenzene?

A Question to Wonder About

Why do the heating curve and the cooling curve have the characteristic shape shown by your graph?

Organizing the Information Collected

In the evaluation of this experiment it helps to record the data in graphical form. Use a full page of your notebook for this, presenting time along the horizontal axis (the abscissa), and using four spaces for one minute. Present temperature on the vertical axis (the ordinate), allowing five spaces for each ten degrees. This scale is chosen in order that the range of data plotted on the horizontal and vertical axes will be approximately equal.

Plot heating and cooling temperatures on the same graph, starting your plotting from the left edge of the graph. For each cooling temperature and its corresponding time, make a small cross. For the heating data use small circles so you can distinguish between plotted points. The temperature fixes how far up on the graph the point is made. The time fixes how far to the right the point is made. This process is called "plotting points."

Using a red pencil, draw a smooth curve to represent heating behavior of the *para*dichlorobenzene. Using a black pencil, do the same for the cooling behavior. Be sure the graph has a title as well as labels on the axes. At the top of the graph sheet give your name, your partner's name, the date, and the name of your experiment.

Study your experimental results as shown in the graph. Write a summary report on the experiment. In the first paragraph tell the results (describe your graph). In the second paragraph give your interpretation of the shape of the heating and cooling curves. Include the graph with your report.

ADDITIONAL INVESTIGATIONS—*to be undertaken as extracurricular experiments. Consult your teacher before proceeding.*

1. Devise an experiment in which you can obtain data to plot a heating curve for the evaporation of a liquid substance. If you use a liquid which does not mix with water you can investigate the behavior of a liquid as it evaporates in a similar manner to that you used for a melting solid in Part II of Experiment 3.

2. Determine the cooling and warming behavior for another solid substance.

4

COMBUSTION OF A CANDLE:
A CLASS EXPERIMENT

This experiment will be performed as a class experiment. Your teacher will do the actual manipulating of equipment while you make the observations and record them in your laboratory notebook.

In your description of a candle, some of your recorded observations probably were: . . . the candle decreases in length as it burns . . . the candle material is consumed. . . . What is happening to the candle and what is causing it to happen? These are questions with a ready answer, too. We all know the candle is burning. But what does this word "burning" really mean? Let's try some experiments to find out.

PROCEDURE

Part I

a. Invert a large (1000 ml) beaker or jar over a burning candle and leave it there until the candle is extinguished. (See Fig. 4-1.) Test the thin liquid film with a strip of cobalt chloride test paper.
b. Moisten a second piece of cobalt chloride test paper with a drop of tap water.

Part II

a. Determine the length of time (seconds) a candle continues to burn when a quart jar or liter beaker is placed over it as shown in Fig. 4-2.
b. Relight the candle and repeat procedure *a*, using a pint jar or 500 ml beaker in place of the quart jar or 1000 ml beaker.

As often happens in science, the attempt to answer one question raises others. What causes the candle flame to be extinguished when confined for a short time? Here are two possible answers:

(1) The burning process *produces* a gaseous material which somehow "quenches" the flame.

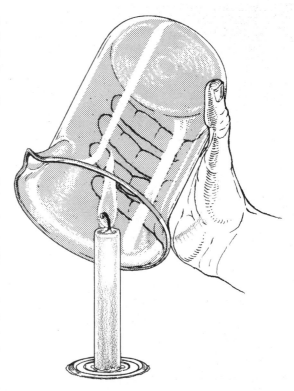

Fig. 4-1. **Testing for a product of combustion.**

7

Fig. 4-2. **Combustion inside a container.**

(2) The burning process *consumes* a gaseous material present in air. When this component of air is gone, the burning ceases.

Part III

a. Using a blowpipe, add air to a candle flame to product a jet. (See Fig. 4-3.)

b. Place a 250 ml Erlenmeyer flask over a burning candle as in Part II procedure *a*. After the candle flame is extinguished, quickly place the flask upright on the table. Obtain a second, clean 250 ml Erlenmeyer flask to be used as a control. Add about 25 ml of limewater solution to each of the flasks. Swirl the solution in each flask simultaneously until a change occurs in one of the flasks.

c. Using a glass tube or a straw, blow your breath into a third flask containing some limewater solution.

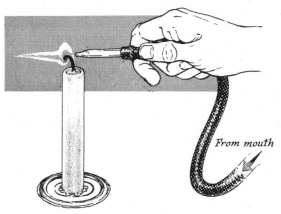

Fig. 4-3. **Blowing air into the flame.**

QUESTIONS

Part I

1. What conclusions can be drawn from this experiment?

2. Does the evidence you have gathered eliminate the possibility that something other than water caused the observed changes? Explain your answer.

3. If the liquid film is water, where does it come from?

4. Would you expect water to be produced if an electric heater were used in place of the candle under the beaker? Explain your answer.

Part II

5. How does the time required to extinguish the candle flame using the quart jar or liter beaker compare to the time using the pint jar or 500 ml beaker?

Part III

6. Explain how these experiments offer a basis for preference between the two answers postulated in Part II for the following question: "What causes the candle flame to be extinguished when confined for a short time in a flask?"

7. Name some possible products of combustion for candle material as indicated by these experiments.

OPTIONAL HOME EXPERIMENT

Refer to Appendix 6, Experiment 4*a*, for suggested home experiments concerning further study of the properties of a burning candle.

5

HEAT EFFECTS

In Experiment 3 we found that the temperature of a melting solid or freezing liquid remains constant as long as the two phases, liquid and solid, are present. The energy that was required to change the solid to a liquid was released when the substance changed from a liquid to a solid. The change that occurs when a solid melts or a liquid freezes is an example of a **phase change**. In Experiment 4 on the combustion products of a candle you found that the candle wax, on burning, changes into at least three substances (finely divided carbon, carbon dioxide, and water). These products have a different composition from the starting materials. This type of change in which new products are formed is called a **chemical change**.

How do these two types of change differ? How are they similar? As a start in answering these questions, let us explore one aspect of behavior: the heat effects accompanying these changes. We shall be primarily concerned with the relative amounts of heat accompanying these two types of changes.

When heat is absorbed by liquid water, the temperature of the water rises. The amount of heat necessary to raise the temperature of one gram of water by one degree Centigrade is reasonably constant between 8°C and 80°C. Consequently, it provides a simple and reproducible basis for a definition of a standard amount of heat, the calorie. A **calorie** is the amount of heat necessary to raise the temperature of one gram of water one degree Centigrade (at about 15°C). Conversely, one calorie is released as one gram of water is cooled one degree Centigrade.

Half of the class will do Part I of this experiment while the other half is doing Part II. Your teacher will tell you which part to do.

Part I. Heat of Combustion

In this experiment you will determine the amount of heat (number of calories) liberated when a candle burns. The amount of candle used is determined by weighing the candle before and after a part of it has been burned. The heat obtained from the candle is used to warm a weighed amount of water. See page ix for instructions on the preparation of a data table before coming to the laboratory.

PROCEDURE

a. Stick a candle to a tin can lid and weigh them on a suitable balance to the nearest 0.01 g. (See Fig. 5-1.) Record the weight of the candle in your data table. Note the balance number so when you weigh the candle again you can use the same balance. This helps to minimize the error due to differences between balances.

b. Weigh an empty can on a platform balance to the nearest 1 g. The can must have two holes punched in it as shown in Fig. 5-2. Record the weight in your data table.

c. Set up the apparatus as shown in Fig. 5-3 such that the flame of the candle when lit (do not light it yet) will almost but not quite touch the bottom of the can. For the chimney use a large can opened at both ends and with two or three holes punched near the bottom for ventilation.

d. Fill the weighed can about two-thirds full with cold tap water. Do not measure the weight or volume of the water at this time.

e. Cool the water with ice, if necessary, so that its temperature is about 10–15°C below room temperature. Add the ice directly to the water. Remove any remaining ice when the desired temperature has been reached.

f. Read and record the temperature of the water to the nearest 0.2°C. Light the candle and heat the water, stirring it gently, until it reaches a temperature about as much above room temperature as it was below at the start. Carefully

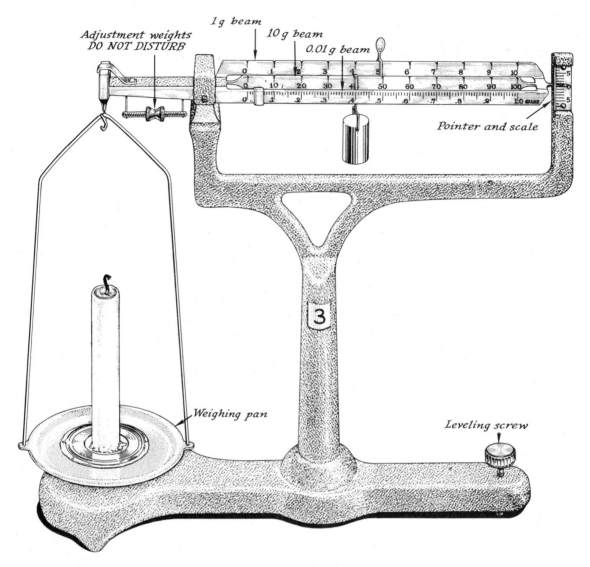

Fig. 5-1. **Weighing a candle** *on a centigram balance. The weights on the balance beams are set at 45.03 g.*

blow out the candle flame. Continue to stir the water, while watching the thermometer reading, until the highest temperature is reached. Record the highest temperature, as before, to the nearest 0.2°C.

g. Weigh the candle on the same balance that was used to weigh it before. Make certain that any drippings from the candle are weighed with it. Record the weight.

h. Weigh the can and water on the same platform balance that was used before, and record this weight. Repeat the experiment if time permits.

Before coming to the laboratory, prepare a

data table in your laboratory notebook which will include the following items:

Centigram balance number_____
Platform balance number _____
Weight of candle before burning (g)
Weight of candle after burning (g)
Weight of can and water (g)
Weight of empty can (g)
Temperature of water before heating (°C)
Temperature of water after heating (°C)
Room temperature (°C)

This will enable you to make the following calculations:

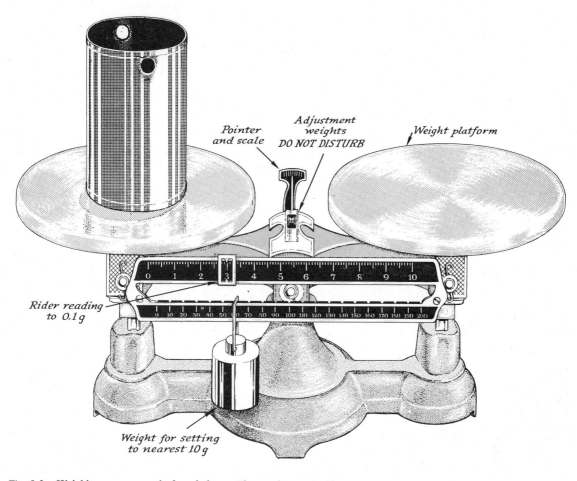

Fig. 5-2. **Weighing a can** *on a platform balance. The weights on the balance beams are set at 63.0 g.*

Weight of candle burned (g)

Weight of water heated (g)

Temperature change of water (Δt)* (°C)

Quantity of heat required to warm the water (calories)† (Assume that all heat from the burning candle was used in heating the water only.)

Heat of combustion of the candle material (calories per gram)

---

*The Greek letter Δ (delta) is often used to represent the change in a quantity. Here, Δt means the change in temperature.

†One calorie of heat will change the temperature of 1 g of water one degree Centigrade. Ten calories of heat will change the temperature of 1 g of water ten degrees Centigrade. One-hundred calories of heat will change the temperature of ten grams of water ten degrees Centigrade. The quantity of heat (calories) is obtained by multiplying the temperature change, Δt, by the weight of the water in grams.

Part II. Heat of Solidification

In this experiment you will use some melted wax, at its melting point, to produce a change in the temperature of a weighed amount of water. See page 13 for instructions on the preparation of a data table before coming to the laboratory.

PROCEDURE

a. Obtain an 18 × 150 millimeter (mm) test tube partially filled with wax (about 10 g of wax). Weigh the test tube with the wax to the nearest 0.1 g. Record the weight.

b. On the same balance, weigh a similar, clean, dry test tube, provided by your teacher, to determine the approximate weight of an empty test tube. Record the weight to the nearest 0.1 g.

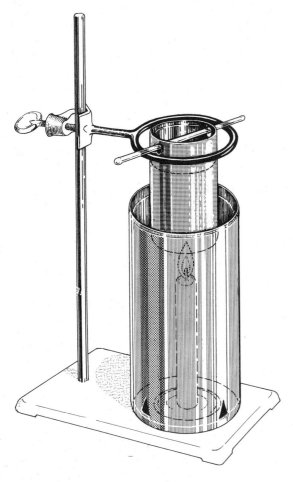

Fig. 5-3. **Apparatus for determining the heat of combustion.**

First sign of cloudiness

Fig. 5-4. **Cooling the wax until solidification begins.**

to the nearest 0.2°C. Quickly place the test tube containing the slightly cloudy wax into the beaker calorimeter and stir the water gently with the test tube. (See Fig. 5-5.) Note the temperature of the water as you stir and continue to observe the temperature until no further increase is noted. (When reading the thermometer, immerse it in the water midway between the test tube and the wall of the beaker.) Record this maximum temperature to the nearest 0.2°C. Repeat the experiment if time permits.

Before coming to the laboratory, prepare a data table in your laboratory notebook which

c. On a platform balance weigh an empty 250 ml beaker which will be used as a calorimeter. Record this weight to the nearest 1 g.

d. Fill the beaker about half full with cold tap water. Use ice, if necessary, to adjust the temperature of the tap water to 1 or 2°C below room temperature. Weigh the beaker and water using the same balance. Record the weight.

e. Heat a second 250 ml beaker, or a small tin can, about half full of water to boiling and place the wax-filled test tube into the boiling water bath until the wax is just melted. Avoid overheating.

f. Using a test tube holder, remove the test tube containing the melted wax from the hot water. Allow the wax to cool until the first sign of cloudiness (solidification) is evident. (See Fig. 5-4.) While the wax is cooling, measure and record the temperature of the cold water bath

Fig. 5-5. **Determining the heat of solidification.**

will include the following items:

Centigram balance number _____
Platform balance number _____
Weight of test tube + wax (g)
Weight of empty test tube (g)
Weight of beaker + water (g)
Weight of empty beaker (g)
Temperature of water before (°C)
Temperature of water after (°C)

This will enable you to make the following calculations:

Weight of wax (g)
Weight of water (g)
Temperature change of water (Δt)*
Quantity of heat required to change the temperature of the water (calories)*. (Neglect the heat required to change the temperature of the beaker Δt.)
Heat of solidification of the wax (calories per gram). (Assume that all of the heat exchanged between the wax and the water is the heat of solidification.)

_____
*See footnotes on page 11.

QUESTIONS FOR EITHER PART I OR PART II

1. Considering the assumptions made in either the "heat of solidification" or "heat of combustion" calculation, would you expect your results to be lower than or higher than the accepted value? Explain.

2. Compare the class averages for heat of combustion and heat of solidification. How much larger is one than the other?

A Question to Wonder About

Why is the heat of combustion so different from the heat accompanying the phase change?

ADDITIONAL INVESTIGATIONS—*to be undertaken as extracurricular experiments. Consult your teacher before proceeding.*

1. Devise an experiment to measure the heat effect for the phase change—gas to liquid—or liquid to gas—for some suitable substance.

2. Devise suitable refinements in Part I of Experiment 5 to eliminate the major sources of error you encountered. Determine the heat of combustion of a pure substance, such as stearic acid, and then compare your results with data that you find in the literature.

6

THE WEIGHTS OF EQUAL VOLUMES OF GASES

Gases seem to be weightless. Yet, if a gas is composed of molecules, the molecules must have substance, hence they must have weight. If this is so, a gas does have weight. Can a gas be weighed with ordinary laboratory balances? If so, do different gases have the same or different weights? Experiment holds the answer.

In this experiment you will have an opportunity to attempt to weigh equal volumes of some gases: oxygen, carbon dioxide, and, perhaps, another gas. Since the volume of a gas varies with its temperature and pressure (conditions that

matter), precautions must be taken to keep these variables the same when the gases are weighed. Since the weight of the gas samples will be at most only a few grams, great care must be taken to avoid sources of error in weighing. A few greasy finger marks or a moisture droplet provides quite enough weight to interfere with the experiment.

Before coming to the laboratory read the experimental directions carefully and organize a table for recording the data and your calculated results.

PROCEDURE

Part I. Weighing Oxygen Gas

a. Obtain a one-hole rubber stopper (size 5 or 6) with a deep groove cut around it about 1 cm from the large end. Fold, in small pleats, the open end of a plastic bag (one-quart size) around the large end of the stopper and hold it firmly in place with a rubber band. See Fig. 6-1.

b. Remove the rubber cap from a medicine dropper. Hold the glass portion with a towel (see Appendix 2, Fig. 2-4) and carefully twist the tapered end of the dropper part of the way into the small end of the stopper until it is firmly held.

c. Press out any air in the bag by smoothing it flat. Replace the rubber cap on the medicine

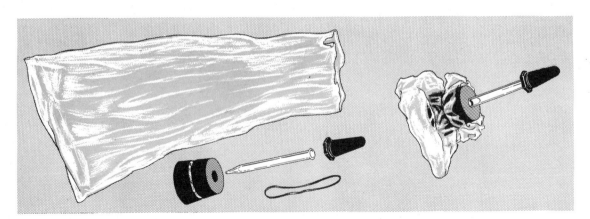

Fig. 6-1. **Making the plastic bag assembly.**

dropper, and weigh this assembly to the nearest 0.01 g. Record the uncertainty as ±0.01 g.

d. Remove the rubber cap and connect the assembly to an oxygen gas source supplied by your teacher. Allow the bag to be fully inflated. See Fig. 6-2. Hold the bag assembly by the stopper and disconnect the rubber tubing from the medicine dropper. Allow any excess gas to escape so the gas in the bag will be at room pressure, but do not squeeze the bag. Then replace the rubber cap.

e. Weigh the bag assembly containing the gas at room temperature and pressure to the nearest 0.01 g. Record the uncertainty as before. *Optional:* If directed by your teacher, repeat steps d and e to check your work.

Part II. Weighing Carbon Dioxide Gas

Be sure the bag and stopper assembly is empty and dry. Fill it with carbon dioxide gas using the source supplied by your teacher. Repeat steps d and e of Part I. Try to have the same volume of gas at the same temperature and pressure as

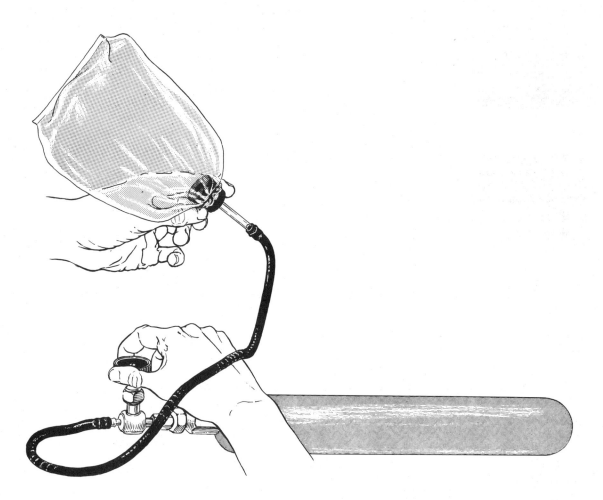

Fig. 6-2. **Filling the plastic bag with a gas.**

before. Repeat the filling with carbon dioxide and weigh the bag assembly again if instructed by your teacher to do this.

Part III. Optional

Obtain the weight of a bag full of another gas if one is available.

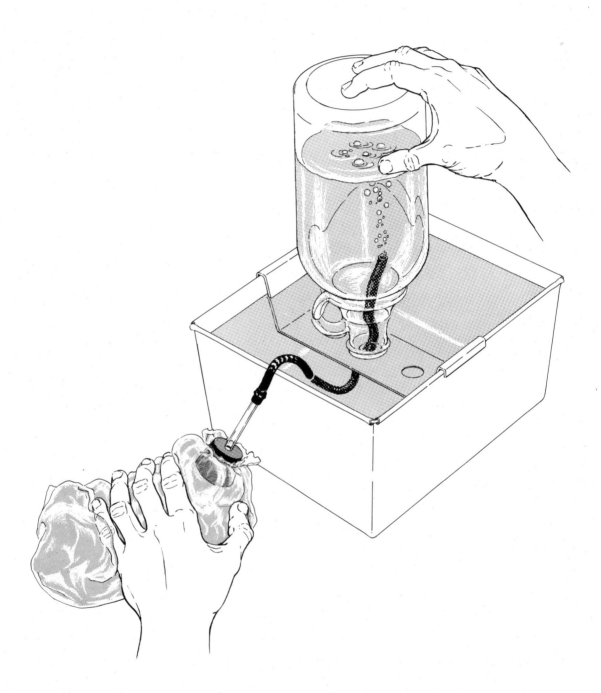

Fig. 6-3. **Measuring the volume of the plastic bag.**

OBTAINING THE VOLUME OF THE BAG

If the bag contains a gas other than oxygen, remove the gas. Then fill the bag with air by blowing into it. Try to have the same volume of gas as you used in each of the previous experiments.

a. Measure the volume of air or oxygen in the bag by the method shown in Fig. 6-3. Completely fill a large bottle or jug (about ½ gallon size) with tap water. Fit it with a stopper and invert it in a large container of water. Remove the stopper under the water.

b. Remove the cap from the medicine dropper and in its place attach a length of rubber tub-

ing. Put the other end of the hose into the neck of the inverted bottle.

c. Gently press on the bag so the gas will displace the water in the bottle. Finally smooth out the bag to remove all the gas.

d. Pinch the tubing to close it and remove it from the water container. Place a solid stopper in the neck of the bottle. Remove the bottle from the water and set it upright on the table.

e. Measure the amount of water required to refill the bottle, using the largest graduated cylinder available to you. Record the volume of the gas displaced and the uncertainty of this measurement.

f. Record the room temperature and pressure.

CALCULATIONS

The Effect of Buoyancy of Air on Weighings

Since we live in an atmosphere of air, we usually do not consider its effects on measurements. For example, when a solid object is weighed in air it is buoyed up by a force equal to the weight of the volume of air it displaces. We usually neglect this fact since the effect is relatively small.

Suppose the medium surrounding us were water. You have probably noticed that objects are easier to lift when they are submerged in water than when they are in air. The water buoys up the submerged object with a force equal to the weight of the volume of water which the object displaces. For example, an object with a volume of 1 liter (1000 ml) when submerged in water displaces a liter of water, so it is buoyed up with a force of 1000 g, the weight of a liter of water. The same object in air is buoyed up with a force of about 1.2 g, the weight of the liter of air it displaces.

In this experiment the apparent weight that you recorded for the weight of the gas did not allow for the buoyant effect of the air. The weight of the volume of air displaced must be added to obtain the actual weight.

The weight of the volume of air displaced can be computed by using the experimentally determined volume of the bag in liters and the weight of a liter of dry air at the appropriate temperature and pressure. See Table 6-1.

Table 6-1

WEIGHT OF A LITER OF AIR IN GRAMS PER LITER, ± 0.01 g, AT VARIOUS TEMPERATURES AND PRESSURES

Pressure (mm)	Temperature			
	15°C	20°C	25°C	30°C
600	0.97	0.95	0.94	0.92
610	0.98	0.97	0.95	0.93
620	1.00	0.98	0.97	0.95
630	1.02	1.00	0.98	0.97
640	1.03	1.01	1.00	0.98
650	1.05	1.03	1.01	1.00
660	1.06	1.05	1.03	1.01
670	1.08	1.06	1.04	1.03
680	1.10	1.08	1.06	1.04
690	1.11	1.09	1.07	1.06
700	1.13	1.11	1.09	1.07
710	1.14	1.12	1.10	1.09
720	1.16	1.14	1.12	1.10
730	1.18	1.16	1.14	1.12
740	1.19	1.17	1.15	1.13
750	1.21	1.19	1.17	1.15
760	1.23	1.21	1.19	1.16
770	1.24	1.22	1.20	1.18

Calculated Results

1. What is the apparent weight of oxygen in the bag? (Subtract the weight of the empty bag from the weight of the bag full of oxygen.)

2. Calculate the weight of the air displaced by the bag filled with gas. Indicate the uncertainty in this derived result. (Refer to Appendix 4.)

3. What is the actual weight of oxygen in the bag? (Add the weight of the air displaced to the apparent weight recorded from the balance.)

4. In a similar way determine the weight of carbon dioxide gas in the bag and the weight of any other gas used.

5. Compare the weight of each gas measured to that of oxygen by dividing each weight by the weight of the comparable volume of oxygen. Express each ratio as a decimal fraction. Include the uncertainty in this derived result.

A Question to Wonder About

Is there any relation between the comparative weights of equal volumes of gases and the relative weight of molecules?

ADDITIONAL INVESTIGATIONS—*to be undertaken as extracurricular experiments. Consult your teacher before proceeding.*

1. How do the weights (of equal volumes) of gases at atmospheric pressure but at higher than ordinary temperatures compare with those at room temperatures?

2. The burner gas in the laboratory is ordinarily natural gas, which is mostly methane, CH_4, but contains some ethane, C_2H_6, and small amounts of other compounds. Weigh a sample of burner gas and calculate the percentage of methane and of ethane, assuming that they are the only gases present.

7

THE BEHAVIOR OF SOLID COPPER IMMERSED IN A WATER SOLUTION OF THE COMPOUND SILVER NITRATE

In this experiment you will weigh a sample of solid silver nitrate and prepare a water solution of it. You will also weigh a piece of copper wire, place it in the solution, and observe its behavior. By weighing the copper wire at the close of the experiment you will be able to investigate quantitatively any changes that occur.

In keeping with chemical practice, we will refer to the chemical substances by using appropriate symbols. Copper is an element; it contains only one kind of atom. The symbol for copper is Cu.

Silver nitrate is a compound and the fo[llowing] identifies it by using the symbol Ag for the [silver] part and the symbols NO_3 for the nitrate [part]. The group of atoms NO_3, consisting of one [nitro]gen atom and three oxygen atoms, are [often] found together in chemical compounds and [is given] the name nitrate.

Before coming to the laboratory, prepa[re a] table in your laboratory notebook so you [can] record the data you will observe. Use the h[ead]ings suggested at the end of the procedure sect[ion].

PROCEDURE

a. Obtain a 30 cm length of copper wire, Cu (No. 16 is suitable). Form a coil by wrapping the wire around a large test tube, leaving about 7 cm straight for a handle. Stretch the coil a little so there is some space between the loops (See Fig. 7-1). Weigh the copper coil to the nearest 0.01 g.

b. Weigh a clean, thoroughly dry 250 ml beaker to the nearest 0.01 g. Weigh the vial of silver nitrate, $AgNO_3$, provided by your teacher.

c. Fill the weighed 250 ml beaker about two-fifths full with *distilled* water. Add the solid silver nitrate, $AgNO_3$, to the water. Stir gently with a solid glass rod until all of the $AgNO_3$ crystals have dissolved. Weigh the empty vial.

Caution: Silver nitrate, solid or solution, reacts with skin and will stain it black. Be careful and avoid spillage on your skin and clothing. However, don't be alarmed if you discover dark spots on your hands—they wear away in a few days. Clean hands the day fol-lowing this experiment indicate good labo[ra]tory technique.

d. Bend the handle of the weighed copper w[ire] such that it can be hung over the edge of [the] beaker with the coil immersed in the AgN[O₃] solution. Place the coil into the beaker a[nd] observe any changes that take place for se[v]eral minutes at least.

e. Cover the beaker with a watch glass and pla[ce] it in your locker until the next laborato[ry] period.

f. At the beginning of the next laboratory perio[d] very carefully open your locker and lift th[e] beaker to the desk top. Observe what has hap[]pened in the beaker. Record *all* your observa[]tions in your laboratory notebook.

g. Shake the crystals off the coil and lift the coi[l] from the solution. Use your wash bottle to[] rinse into the beaker any crystals which tend[] to adhere to the coil. See Fig. 7-1. Set the coil[] aside to dry. Weigh it when dry.

Fig. 7-1. **Rinsing with a wash bottle.**

h. Let the crystals settle in the beaker. Carefully decant the solution. Decant means to pour off liquid, leaving solid behind, as shown in Fig. 7-2. Add 5 ml of dilute silver nitrate solution and stir gently until any flecks of copper disappear. Carefully decant again. Wash the residue with 10 ml of water and carefully decant. Wash and decant at least three more times. You may neglect the few particles which may float over with the wash water since the amount is usually not weighable.
Optional: Save the solution decanted first for possible further experimentation suggested at the end of this experiment.

i. After the final washing, the residue must be dried. Your teacher will suggest a suitable method. If the sample is dried overnight with heat lamps or in a drying oven, it should be dry when you return to the laboratory.

   Allow the beaker and contents to cool before weighing. Use the same balance as you used previously and record the weight together with the uncertainty.
Note: If a sand bath is used to dry the sample, you can make sure that it is dry as follows. Weigh the sample and beaker, then return the

sample to the sand bath and heat it for a second time. Weigh it again. If weight was lost, you did not have a dry sample and it may not be dry this time, so heat and weigh it again. Repeat the procedure until a constant weight is obtained.

j. Cover the dry solid in the beaker with a watch glass and save it for Experiment 8.

Your data table should include the following (be sure to include uncertainty as part of your recorded data):

Weight of copper before immersion in solution
Weight of copper at close of experiment
Weight change of copper
Weight of vial plus silver nitrate
Weight of vial
Weight of silver nitrate
Weight of beaker plus silver
Weight of beaker
Weight of silver

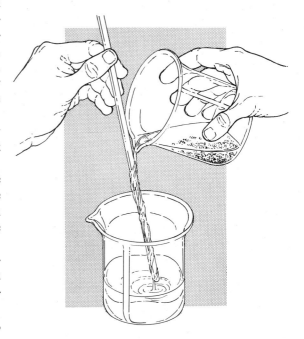

Fig. 7-2. **Decanting the supernatant liquid from the residue.**

CALCULATIONS

Reread Sections 2-3.3 and 2-3.4 in the text before proceeding with the calculations.

1. Calculate the number of moles of copper which reacted. Recall, as in the Textbook Exercise 2–9, that the weight of a substance divided by the weight per mole equals the number of moles.

2. Calculate the number of moles of silver obtained.

3. Determine the ratio of moles of silver to moles of copper involved in this reaction. Be sure to express your calculations using the correct number of significant figures.

QUESTIONS

1. What you have observed can be described by the following statement:

   One mole of copper *(solid)* +_____mole(s) of silver nitrate *(in water)* ⟶ _____mole(s) of silver *(solid)* + _____mole(s) of copper nitrate *(in water)*.

   Using the results obtained in this experiment, write the proper whole number coefficients in the above statement when 1 mole of copper is used up.

2. How many atoms of solid copper were involved in *your* experiment? See Section 2-3.3 in the Textbook.

3. How many atoms of solid silver were involved in *your* experiment?

4. What is the relationship between the number of atoms of silver and the number of atoms of copper calculated in questions 2 and 3?

5. In order to evaluate the results of this experiment, your teacher will collect the data obtained by other members of your class. Make a graph, plotting the number of individuals obtaining a given silver/copper ratio along the vertical axis. Plot the Ag/Cu ratios along the horizontal axis. These should be rounded off so that each division on the graph will represent values of ±0.05. For example,

values from 1.85 up to but not including 1.95 should be plotted as 1.9.

6. Considering only the middle two-thirds of the data plotted, what is the range of values obtained? How does this compare with the uncertainty you considered justifiable from your measurements?

Questions to Wonder About

1. What causes the color in the solution after the reaction is completed?

2. What is the nature of the particles in aqueous solution?

ADDITIONAL INVESTIGATIONS—*to be undertaken as extracurricular experiments. Consult your teacher before proceeding.*

Divide the "blue solution" obtained in step *h* into two approximately equal portions so you can make the following investigations.

1. Carefully evaporate the solution to dryness and observe the product.

2. Place a piece of a metallic substance into the blue solution. Observe any changes which occur immediately and after a day or so.

MASS RELATIONSHIPS ACCOMPANYING CHEMICAL CHANGES

In this experiment you will use the silver you produced in Experiment 7 to form a water solution of silver nitrate, $AgNO_3$, by allowing the silver to react with nitric acid, HNO_3. You will next prepare a water solution of sodium chloride, NaCl, add it to the silver nitrate solution and weigh the products formed.

You will review and learn many techniques: careful weighing, decanting, filtering, washing, and drying. Carry them out well, for it will be assumed in future work that you are able to use these techniques.

Record your data carefully and neatly. Take special care to show the units used in your measurements. Include the uncertainty in each measurement. Before you come to the lab to do an experiment, you should have planned what you are to do. This preparation will free your mind from mechanical details and allow you to concentrate on making the required observations in the allotted time.

PROCEDURE

Part I. Preparation of Solid Silver Nitrate from Metallic Silver

a. Refer back to Experiment 7 and record the weight of the beaker used (label this #1), the weight of the silver nitrate used, and the weight of the silver produced.

b. To the beaker containing the silver, add 10 ml of nitric acid, labeled 6 M* HNO_3. Avoid inhaling any of the poisonous reddish-brown fumes of nitrogen dioxide, NO_2, which form as the silver dissolves. Identify your beaker with your name or locker number and leave it in the fume hood or near an open window overnight to be evaporated to dryness.

c. When it is dry, weigh the beaker which now contains $AgNO_3$. Remember the caution given in Experiment 7 concerning the handling of silver nitrate.

Part II. The Effect of Adding a Solution of Sodium Chloride to a Solution of Silver Nitrate.

a. Add about 15 ml of distilled water to the

$AgNO_3$ in beaker #1. Stir until no more change takes place.

b. Remove from the stock bottle about 2–2½ grams (approximately ½ teaspoonful) of sodium chloride, NaCl, as shown in Fig. 8-1.

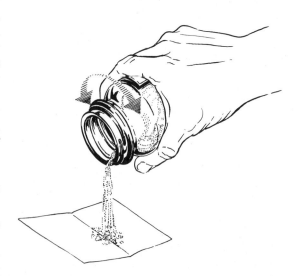

Fig. 8-1. **Rotate the bottle** *to obtain the approximate amount of solid.*

---

*The term 6 M refers to the concentration of the solution, which is defined in Chapter 5 of the Textbook. This solution is moderately concentrated so be sure to wash it off your skin or clothes if it is spilled and off the graduate before you put it away.

Gently rotate the bottle back and forth to pour out the approximate amount needed on a piece of clean paper.

c. Label a clean, dry 100 ml beaker as #2 and weigh it to the nearest 0.01 g.

d. Adjust your balance so it reads somewhere between 2 and 2.5 grams greater than the weight of beaker #2, and add carefully enough table salt, NaCl, from the paper to make the balance pan drop. Discard any salt remaining on the paper, then determine the weight of the NaCl and beaker to the nearest 0.01 g. (See Fig. 8-2.)

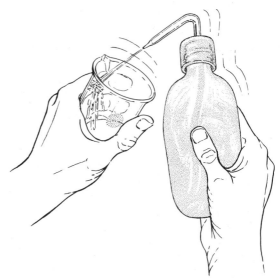

Fig. 8-3. **Rinsing the beaker with a wash bottle.**

g. Heat the resulting precipitate (the solid which settles out) and the solution to boiling for about 2 minutes or until the solution becomes reasonably clear as the precipitate settles. Place a stirring rod in the beaker to help prevent unsteady boiling (bumping).

h. Determine the weight of a piece of filter paper to the nearest 0.01 g. Fold it as shown in Fig. 8-4. Fit it into a funnel and moisten the paper with some distilled water from a wash bottle. Set up the funnel for filtering as shown in Fig. 8-5.

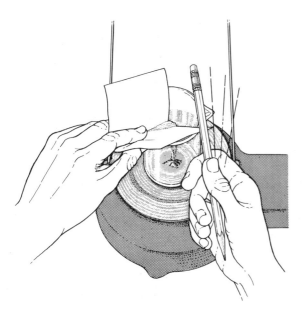

Fig. 8-2. **Weighing a desired amount.**

e. Add about 15 ml of distilled water to the solid NaCl. Stir until no more change takes place.

f. While briskly stirring the AgNO₃ solution in beaker #1, slowly add the NaCl solution. Note the result. The white solid produced is the compound silver chloride, AgCl. Rinse the empty beaker, #2, with about 5 ml of distilled water from the wash bottle by directing the water around the inside of the beaker (see Fig. 8-3). Add the rinse water to the mixture in beaker #1. Rinse beaker #2 again with distilled water and this time discard the rinse water. The clean beaker will be used again in step *i*.

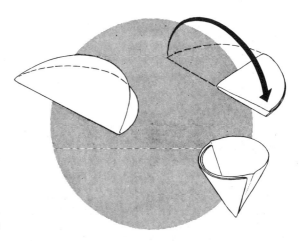

Fig. 8-4. **Folding a piece of filter paper.**

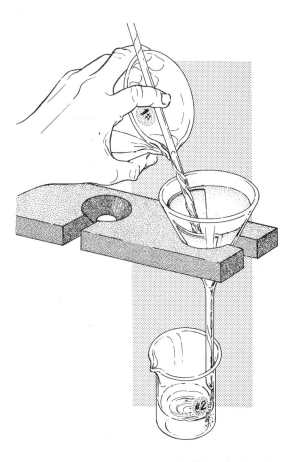

Fig. 8-5.   **Pouring the supernatant liquid into the funnel.**

i. Place beaker #2 under the funnel. The tip of
   the funnel should touch the beaker so a steady
   stream can run down the side. Decant the
   clear *liquid* from beaker #1 into the funnel,
   pouring it into the funnel along a glass rod.

A small amount of the precipitate may transfer to the filter paper, but try to keep most of
it in the beaker where it can be washed more
readily.

j. Wash the precipitate in the beaker with about
   15 ml of distilled water, stirring with a glass
   rod to aid the washing. Decant the wash water
   into the funnel. Repeat the washing procedure
   with another 15 ml of water. Decant the wash
   water again into the funnel.

k. After the filtration is complete, place the filter
   paper and any solid it contains in beaker #1
   containing the precipitate.

l. Place both samples, the filtrate (the solution
   passing through the filter) in beaker #2 and
   the wet precipitate in beaker #1, in the place
   designated by your teacher for evaporation
   and drying overnight. Be sure each beaker is
   numbered and has your name or locker number on it.

m. Weigh both dry samples and record the
   weights. Save the silver chloride as directed
   by your teacher.

Your data table should include the following:

Weight of silver from Experiment 7
Weight of silver nitrate used in Experiment 7
Weight of beaker #1
Weight of beaker #1 and solid $AgNO_3$
Weight of beaker #1, filter paper, and solid
   AgCl
Weight of beaker #2
Weight of beaker #2 and solid NaCl
Weight of a piece of filter paper
Weight of beaker #2 and solid residue

CALCULATIONS AND RESULTS

	Weight in grams	Number of moles
Ag (from Experiment 7)	—	—
$AgNO_3$ (used in Experiment 7)	—	no entry
$AgNO_3$ (produced in Experiment 8)	—	—
NaCl (added)	—	—
AgCl (in beaker #1) (Remember to subtract weight of filter paper)	—	—
Residue (in beaker #2)	—	no entry

QUESTIONS AND EXERCISES

1. How does the weight of $AgNO_3$ produced in this experiment compare with the weight used in Experiment 7? How do you account for any similarity or difference?

2. Compare the sum of the weights of the $AgNO_3$ and NaCl used with the sum of the weights of the AgCl and the residue in beaker #2. Your conclusions will be more meaningful if they are based on class data compiled by your teacher. What is the significance of these results?

3. Compare your results for the number of moles of silver used, of silver nitrate produced in Part I, and of silver chloride produced in Part II by computing the ratio between the moles of silver and each of the other substances, $AgNO_3$ and AgCl. Use the nearest whole number to express your result. What can you conclude about the number of moles involved in this series of chemical changes?

4. Pure silver nitrate is a white solid. How do you account for any color which may be present in your sample or in the samples prepared by other students?

ADDITIONAL INVESTIGATION — *to be undertaken as an extracurricular experiment. Consult your teacher before proceeding.*

Devise an experiment to determine the composition of the residue in beaker #2. Study Exercises 3–9 and 3–10 in Chapter 3 of the Textbook as a preliminary step to this investigation.

9

A QUANTITATIVE INVESTIGATION OF THE REACTION OF A METAL WITH HYDROCHLORIC ACID

In this experiment you will determine the volume of hydrogen gas which is produced when a sample of magnesium metal reacts with hydrogen chloride dissolved in water. The volume of the hydrogen gas will be measured at room temperature and pressure—conditions that matter for a gas. The data you obtain will enable you to answer the question: How many liters of dry hydrogen gas at room temperature and 1 atmosphere can be produced per mole of magnesium metal?

PROCEDURE

a. Obtain a piece of magnesium, Mg, ribbon approximately 5 cm long (at high altitudes use a shorter piece). Measure the length of the ribbon carefully and record this to the nearest 0.05 cm. Your teacher will give you the weight of 1 meter of the ribbon, and since it is uniform in thickness you can calculate the weight of the magnesium used.

b. Fold the magnesium ribbon so that it can be encased in a small spiral cage made of fine copper wire. Leave about 5 cm of copper wire to serve as a handle. See Fig. 9-1.

c. Set up a ring stand and utility clamp in position to hold a 50 ml gas measuring tube which has been fitted with a one- or two-hole rubber stopper as shown in Fig. 9-1. Place a 400 ml beaker about two-thirds full of tap water near the ring stand.

d. Incline the gas measuring tube slightly from an upright position and pour in about 10 ml of moderately concentrated hydrochloric acid labeled 6 *M* HCl.

e. With the tube in the same position, slowly fill it with tap water from a beaker. While pouring, rinse any acid that may be on the sides of the tube so that the liquid in the top of the

tube will contain very little acid. Try to avoid stirring up the acid layer in the bottom of the tube. Bubbles clinging to the sides of the tube can be dislodged by tapping the tube gently.

f. Holding the copper coil by the handle, insert the metal about 3 cm down into the tube. Hook the copper wire over the edge of the tube and clamp it there by inserting the rubber stopper. The tube should be completely filled so that the stopper displaces a little water when put in place. See the left of Fig. 9-1.

g. Cover the hole(s) in the stopper with your finger and invert the tube in the container of water, as shown in the middle of Fig. 9-1. Clamp it in place. The acid being more dense than water will diffuse down through it and eventually react with the metal.

h. After the reaction stops, wait for about 5 minutes to allow the tube to come to room temperature. Dislodge any bubbles clinging to the sides of the tube.

i. Cover the hole(s) in the stopper with your finger and transfer the tube to a large cylinder or battery jar which is almost filled with water at room temperature. See Fig. 9-2. Raise or

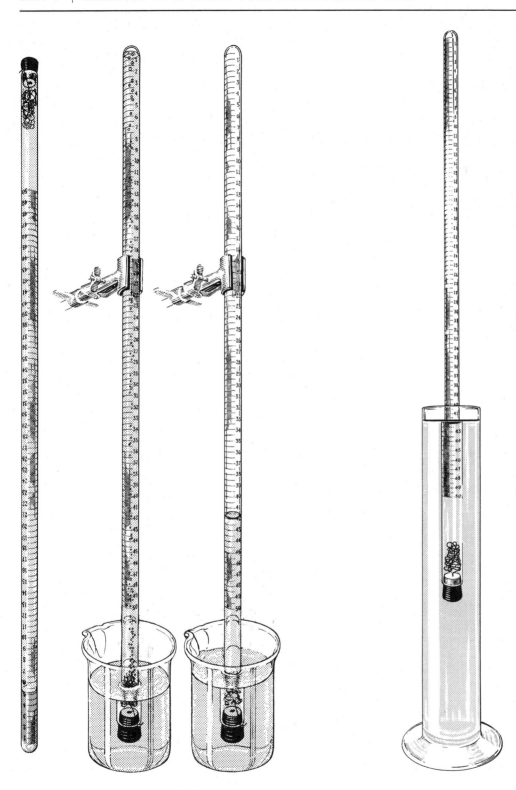

Fig. 9-1. **Manipulating the gas measuring tube.**

Fig. 9-2. **Measuring the volume of gas.**

lower the tube until the level of the liquid inside the tube is the same as the level outside the tube. This permits you to measure the volume of the gases in the tube (hydrogen and water vapor) at room pressure.

Read the volume with your eye at the same level as the bottom of the **meniscus** (the lens shape surface taken by the water in the tube). See Fig. 9-3. Record the volume of the gas to the nearest 0.05 ml.

j. Remove the gas measuring tube from the water and pour the acid solution it contains down the sink. Rinse the tube with tap water.

k. Record the room temperature. Your teacher will give you the room pressure or will assist you in reading the barometer to obtain a value for the pressure in the room.

The experiment may be repeated with another sample of magnesium to check your results, if time permits.

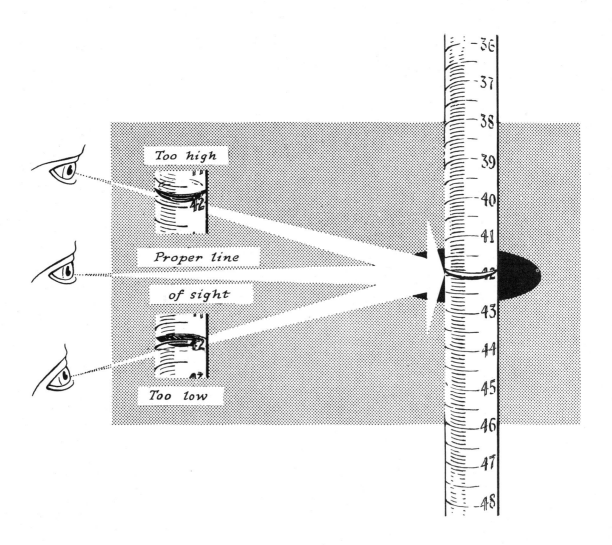

Fig. 9-3. **Read bottom of meniscus** *with eye at proper level.*

The data table should include the following:

Weight of magnesium ribbon in grams per meter (from teacher)
Length of magnesium ribbon
Volume of hydrogen (saturated with water vapor)
Temperature of the water
Temperature of the room
Barometer reading (room pressure)

Vapor pressure of water at the above temperature (see the following table):

VAPOR PRESSURE OF WATER AT VARIOUS TEMPERATURES

Temperature (°C)	Pressure (mm)	Temperature (°C)	Pressure (mm)
15	12.8	23	21.0
16	13.6	24	22.4
17	14.5	25	23.8
18	15.5	26	25.2
19	16.5	27	26.7
20	17.5	28	28.3
21	18.6	29	30.0
22	19.8	30	31.8

CALCULATIONS

1. Determine the weight of the magnesium you used from the grams per meter relationship and the length of the ribbon.

2. Determine the number of moles of magnesium used.

3. Determine the partial pressure of the hydrogen gas.

Since the hydrogen gas was collected over water, the gas in the tube consists of a mixture of hydrogen gas and water vapor. The total pressure caused by these two gases is equal to the room pressure. See the hypothetical case illustrated in Fig. 9-4A. Mathematically this can be expressed

$$P_{H_2} + P_{H_2O} = P_{room}$$

The pressure of the room may be determined by reading the barometer. The pressure of the water vapor, P_{H_2O}, can be determined from the table given above. The values in the table were obtained by measuring the pressure of water vapor above liquid water at various temperatures. The partial pressure of the hydrogen can then be calculated as follows:

$$P_{H_2} = P_{room} - P_{H_2O}$$

See Fig. 9-4B for illustration of the pressure due to the hydrogen alone.

4. Determine the volume of the hydrogen gas at one atmosphere pressure (760 mm).

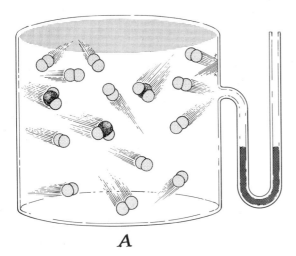

A

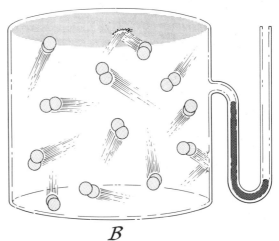

B

Fig. 9-4. **Partial pressure of hydrogen and water vapor.**

You have learned that for a given temperature the product of the pressure and volume of a gas is a constant. $PV = k$. To calculate the new volume, V_{new} at 760 mm pressure, the following mathematical relationship can be stated

$$V_{measured} P_{H_2} = V_{new} 760$$

or

$$V_{new} = V_{measured} \times \frac{P_{H_2}}{760}$$

5. Calculate the volume of dry hydrogen which would be produced by 1 mole of magnesium at room temperature and 1 atmosphere pressure.

QUESTIONS

1. Given that 1 mole of Mg produces 1 mole of hydrogen, H_2, what is the volume of 1 mole of hydrogen at room temperature and 1 atmosphere pressure?

2. If 1 mole of hydrogen weighs 2.0 g, what is the weight of a liter (the density) of hydrogen at room temperature and 1 atmosphere pressure?

ADDITIONAL INVESTIGATION—*To be undertaken as an extracurricular experiment. Consult your teacher before proceeding.*

Determine the volume of hydrogen gas produced when a mole of another metal reacts with an acid.

10

AN INVESTIGATION OF THE REACTING VOLUMES OF TWO SOLUTIONS OF KNOWN CONCENTRATION

In this experiment you will prepare solutions of lead nitrate, $Pb(NO_3)_2$, and sodium iodide, NaI, of known concentration, 0.50 M. You will observe the results which occur when various volumes of these solutions are mixed. From the relative volumes of solutions used and their molarity, and from the weights of the precipitates formed, it will be possible to determine the number of moles of the substances involved in the reactions.

PROCEDURE

Part I. The Preparation of Solutions

In this experiment you will be assigned to work with a partner. Each partner will prepare *one* of the 0.50 M solutions which will be shared as the remainder of the experiment is performed.

a. Before coming to the laboratory, each partner should calculate the weight of each of the compounds lead nitrate, $Pb(NO_3)_2$, and sodium iodide, NaI, needed to make 25.0 ml of a 0.50 M solution of each. Check your answers with those of your partner before proceeding to step *b*.

b. In the laboratory, each partner will weigh the calculated amount of one solid. (Refer back to Fig. 8-1 for a method of transferring an approximate amount of a solid to a piece of paper before attempting to weigh an exact amount.) Fig. 10-1 shows the technique for obtaining the desired amount on a paper on the balance pan. First weigh a clean piece of smooth paper, then adjust the weights so you will obtain the additional weight of the solid needed. Tap the paper containing the approximate amount gently to transfer the solid a little at a time onto the weighed paper on the

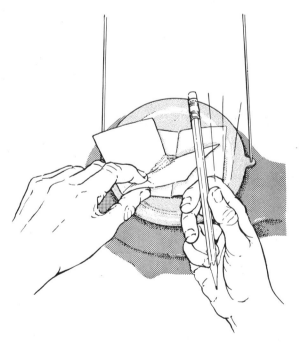

Fig. 10-1. **Tap the paper gently** *to transfer the desired amount.*

balance pan. If you should transfer too much, remove a few crystals with a spatula or a small piece of paper with a fold in the middle.

c. Carefully transfer all of one of the weighed solids to a small clean beaker and dissolve it in about 20 ml of distilled water. Pour the resulting solution into a clean 25 ml or 50 ml graduated cylinder and add just enough distilled water with a clean medicine dropper to make the volume 25.0 ml. (Refer back to Fig. 9-3 for the proper method of reading a meniscus.) *Pour the solution back* into the same beaker used to dissolve the solid, and *stir the solution* gently until it is *uniformly mixed.* If you must reuse the graduate for the second solution, rinse it well. Label each solution.

Part II. A Qualitative Study of the Amounts of Precipitate Formed When Various Volumes of the Solutions are Mixed.

The following table gives the volumes which are to be carefully measured into clean 13 × 100 mm test tubes by the technique described in steps IIa and IIb. One partner should do step *a* while the other goes on to step *b*.

Test Tube	Milliliters of 0.50 M Sodium Iodide	Milliliters of 0.50 M Lead Nitrate
1	4.0	0.5
2	4.0	1.0
3	4.0	2.0
4	4.0	3.0
5	4.0	4.0

a. Measure out the 4.0 ml volumes of sodium iodide solution as follows. Fill a *clean* 10 ml graduated cylinder with the sodium iodide solution so that the meniscus is at the 10.0 ml mark. (Refer back to Fig. 9-3 for the proper method of reading a meniscus.) Use a *clean* medicine dropper to adjust the level if necessary. Use the same empty medicine dropper to withdraw successive portions of the solution from the graduated cylinder, until exactly 4.0 ml has been transferred to one of the labeled test tubes. Repeat this procedure with the other four test tubes.

b. Measure out the various volumes of lead ni-

trate as follows. Fill a *clean* 10 ml graduated cylinder with the lead nitrate solution so that the meniscus is at the 10.0 ml mark. Use a *clean* medicine dropper to adjust the level if necessary. Use the empty medicine dropper to remove exactly 0.5 ml of the solution and transfer it dropwise to test tube 1 prepared by your partner. (See Fig. 10-2.) Place a clean stopper into the test tube and mix the solutions by shaking the tube.

In a similar manner add the volumes 1.0 ml, 2.0 ml, 3.0 ml, and 4.0 ml, respectively, to tubes 2, 3, 4, and 5. Mix each of the solutions well.

c. Set the test tubes in an erect position, and after the precipitates have settled, measure the relative heights of the yellow solid, lead iodide, in each test tube. If time permits, observe the relative heights of the precipitates later in the period or at the beginning of the next laboratory period.

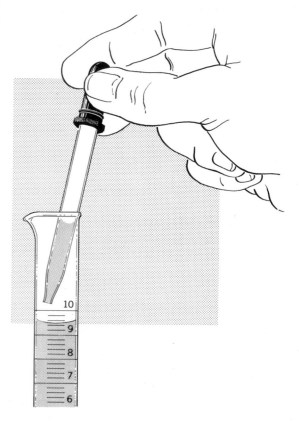

Fig. 10-2. **Calibrating a medicine dropper.**

Part III. The Quantitative Determination of the Weights of Lead Iodide Formed

If there is not time for all the class to do Part III, it should be performed by some selected students or by the teacher so that quantitative results will be available to all students. You and your partner should divide the work of filtering, drying, and weighing the five precipitates in a systematic manner. Each of you should set up a filtering apparatus to save time.

a. Number five pieces of filter paper 1, 2, 3, 4, and 5 to correspond with the numbered test tubes. Weigh the five filter papers and then record the average weight of each in your notebook.

b. Fold filter paper 1 and place it into the funnel as shown in Fig. 8-5. Have a small beaker available under the funnel.

c. Place a stopper into test tube 1 and shake the contents. Remove the stopper and quickly pour the precipitate and solution into the filter cone. Place the *same* test tube under the funnel tip and collect several milliliters of the filtrate. Rinse the walls of the test tube with the filtrate and quickly pour the contents into the filter to remove the remaining lead iodide from the test tube. Repeat the rinsing of the test tube if necessary. Catch the final filtrate in a beaker.

d. When the filter has drained, direct a small stream of distilled water from a wash bottle over the filter paper to rinse away the soluble salt, sodium nitrate, from the filter. (Since lead iodide is slightly soluble in water, 0.063 g/100 ml at 20°C, use as little water as possible.) Discard the filtrate and washings.

e. Finally rinse the test tube and its stopper with 5 ml of ethyl alcohol and pour this over the precipitate on the filter paper to remove some of the water.

f. Remove the filter paper carefully and place it on a paper towel. Carefully blot out some of the moisture. Place the labeled filter cone in your desk and allow it to dry overnight. In some climates it may be necessary to dry the precipitates with heat lamps or by another method suggested by your teacher.

g. Repeat steps *c* through *f* with the precipitates in each of the other four test tubes.

h. Weigh each of the *dry* filter cones containing the lead iodide precipitates. Record the weights in your notebook.

CALCULATIONS AND QUESTIONS

1. Obtain the weight of lead iodide from each test tube by subtracting the weight of one piece of filter paper from the weights recorded in Part III*h*.

2. Plot the data obtained in this experiment on a graph. Plot the grams of lead iodide along the ordinate and the number of milliliters of lead nitrate used along the abscissa.

3. How do you explain the shape of the curve obtained when you connect the plotted points in the graph?

4. Calculate the number of moles of lead nitrate and of sodium iodide used in each of the five test tubes. Tabulate your answers. Two entries have been made for you.

5. Refer to the graph and select the combination in which there was just enough of the lead nitrate solution to react with all of the sodium iodide.

6. Refer to question 4 and determine the ratio of the moles of lead nitrate to the moles of sodium iodide for the combination selected in question 5. Use this ratio to determine the formula of lead iodide.

7. Use the weight of the precipitate obtained in the combination referred to in question 5 to calculate the number of moles of lead iodide produced in this test tube. How does this compare with the number of moles of lead nitrate and of sodium iodide used for this combination?

Test Tube	Moles of $Pb(NO_3)_2$	Moles of NaI
1	0.00025	0.0020
2		
3		
4		
5		

REACTIONS BETWEEN IONS
IN AQUEOUS SOLUTION

Each of the compounds used in this experiment is an ionic solid and its aqueous solution contains positive and negative ions in such proportion that their net electric charge is zero. The actual manipulation of the solutions is simple. You are to mix all possible combinations of a set of six solutions and record the cases where a precipitate is formed.

Organize a table for your observations as shown below. Number each solution and, in a vertical column, write formulas for the pair of ions present in each solution. Write the pairs of formulas again in a horizontal row, but in reverse order this time. The following sample entries are not necessarily the ions you will encounter in your set of solutions.

Kinds of Ions in Solution	6	5	etc.
	K^+, Cl^-	etc.	
1 Ba^{+2}, NO_3^-			
2 Ba^{+2}, Cl^-			
3 etc.			
etc.			

If you do not know the charge associated with each ion, refer to Appendix 9, which gives this information.

With six different solutions, how many different tests will you need to make in order to study all of the possible combinations of solutions, using them two at a time?

PROCEDURE

Method I. Using Small Test Tubes

Place a dropperful, about 1 ml, of one solution in a clean 13 × 100 mm test tube. Add to it the same volume of another solution. If the set of solutions is not provided with individual droppers, be *sure* to rinse the dropper thoroughly before using it in another solution. Continue mixing the solutions, two at a time, until you have tried all of the different combinations.

In the data table, make an entry to indicate those combinations in which a precipitate is formed. Use the abbreviation ppt for precipitate, and a dash, —, when no precipitate is formed.

If directed to do so by your teacher, repeat the above procedure with another set of solutions.

Method II. Using Glass Plates

Place a drop of one solution on a clean, dry glass plate and add a drop of a second solution to it. The glass plate may be marked off in small squares with a wax pencil so that several combinations may be tried on the same plate. Continue until you have tried all possible pairs of solutions from the six provided. On the glass plates, a precipitate will appear as a cloudy suspension.

In the data table, make an entry to indicate those combinations in which a precipitate is formed. Use the abbreviation ppt for precipitate, and a dash, —, when no precipitate is formed.

If directed to do so by your teacher, repeat the above procedure with another set of solutions.

INTERPRETATION OF RESULTS

Since the pairs of ions listed in your data table were present in solution you may assume that each precipitate produced was due to a new combination of ions. For example, if you mix aqueous solutions of $AgNO_3$ and $NaCl$, the ions present are $Ag^+(aq)$, $NO_3^-(aq)$, $Na^+(aq)$, and $Cl^-(aq)$ and the new combinations possible are $AgCl$ and $NaNO_3$. What new combinations were possible in the mixtures producing a precipitate? List these. Note that in each case if a precipitate occurred it could be either of two combinations of ions.

CONCLUSIONS

1. Examine your results and propose explanations that will account for the fact that a precipitate was observed in some cases and not in others.

2. Propose a further experiment to test your ideas.

3. Write equations to indicate what you consider to have happened in each case in which there was a reaction. Use ions to represent the species in the reacting solutions, but for those products that were precipitates write a formula. [Place *(aq)* after those species in solution and *(s)* after the precipitates.] Be sure to write the equations so that both the atoms and charges are conserved.

For example,

$$Ag^+(aq) + NO_3^-(aq) + Na^+(aq) + Cl^-(aq)$$
$$\longrightarrow AgCl(s) + Na^+(aq) + NO_3^-(aq)$$

4. Rewrite these equations, leaving out the ions not involved. Such an equation, showing only the predominant reacting species, is called a net ionic equation.

12

A STUDY OF REACTIONS

What is a chemical reaction?

Early in the course we had an opportunity to observe various kinds of change, one of which was a phase change. When this type of change occurs it does not alter the empirical formula of the substance. For example, ice, $H_2O(s)$, melts to form liquid water, $H_2O(l)$, and evaporates to gaseous water, $H_2O(g)$. On the other hand, a chemical change is one in which the atoms are rearranged to form substances which have empirical formulas different from those of the reactants. Both involve a change in attraction (bonding) between atoms or between groups of atoms called molecules. How do we know when a chemical change has occurred?

In our study of the candle we concluded that a chemical change occurs during burning because the products of combustion (water, carbon dioxide, etc.) have many properties which are different from those of the reactants (candle substance and oxygen in the air). The appearance of a new substance with different properties is a clue that a chemical reaction has occurred. We may observe color changes, gas formation, or products with different solubilities as evidence of changes which occur during reactions.

A second clue is to note the amount of energy involved. You will recall that in Experiment 5 you found that the energy involved in a phase change (heat of solidification) was very much less than that involved in a chemical change (combustion). A chemical reaction in which energy is released is called an "exothermic reaction" and one in which energy is absorbed is called an "endothermic reaction."

Besides looking for evidence that chemical changes have occurred, there are other phenomena accompanying such reactions that you should observe:

(1) The rate of the reaction, that is, how rapidly the change takes place, and what factors affect the rate: temperature, concentration, and the presence of other substances (catalysts).

(2) The completeness of the reaction. Does the reaction continue until most of the reactants are used up?

In this experiment you will mix certain substances together, keeping in mind the above mentioned clues and characteristics which are to be observed in the chemical reactions as they occur.

Refer to items 5, 6, and 7 of the Laboratory Instructions on page ix regarding the precautions to be observed in handling, tasting, and smelling chemicals.

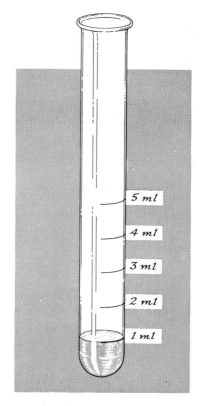

Fig. 12-1. **A full-scale drawing** *of a calibrated 13 x 100 mm test tube.*

Make a table in your laboratory notebook. The table should include:

(1) a description of the reactants involved in each reaction
(2) a rather detailed observation of each reaction and
(3) your reasons for believing a chemical reaction has or has not taken place.

Quantities are to be estimated in this experiment. Mark the volume levels of 1, 2, 3, 4, and 5 milliliters in the test tube you will be using (13 × 100 mm size). Fig. 12-1 is a full scale drawing of a 13 × 100 mm test tube showing various volumes.

PROCEDURE

Part I

a. To 5 ml of tap water in a test tube add 15 drops, a drop at a time, of 18 M sulfuric acid, H_2SO_4. Record your observations. Always add concentrated acid to water; never add water to concentrated acid. Save the diluted acid (about 2 M) to use in Parts IIb and IIIa.
b. To 5 ml of tap water in a test tube add 3 small pellets of solid sodium hydroxide, NaOH(s). *Do not handle sodium hydroxide pellets with your fingers.* Place a stopper in the test tube and shake it gently. Record your observations. Save the solution for Part IIa.
c. To 1 ml of solid ammonium chloride, $NH_4Cl(s)$, in a test tube add 5 ml of tap water. Stopper the tube and shake it gently. Record your observations.
d. Repeat step c, except use 1 ml of solid sodium acetate, $NaCH_3COO(s)$ as the solid.

Part II

a. Add about 1 ml of the sodium hydroxide solution prepared in Part Ib to 5 ml of tap water. Add a few drops of a solution of phenolphthalein (an indicator solution).
b. Repeat the test of step a except use 1 ml of the sulfuric acid solution prepared in Part Ia in place of the sodium hydroxide solution.
c. Place a small amount (about $\frac{1}{4}$ ml) of solid sodium sulfite, Na_2SO_3, in a test tube. Add cautiously about 3 ml of dilute hydrochloric acid, 6 M HCl.
d. Place about 5 ml of 0.1 M acidified ferrous sulfate, $FeSO_4$, in a test tube. Add 10 drops of 0.1 M potassium permanganate, $KMnO_4$, one drop at a time, shaking the test tube after the addition of each drop.

e. Add 1 ml of 0.1 M sodium chloride, NaCl, to 1 ml of 0.1 M potassium bromide, KBr.
f. Place about $\frac{1}{2}$ ml of powdered lead dioxide, PbO_2, in a test tube. Heat over a burner flame and note any changes. Light a wooden splint, blow out the flame, and quickly thrust the splint into the test tube while it is still glowing. How do you account for the result? Set the test tube aside to cool before you rinse it out.

Part III

a. Set up four test tubes, each containing 5 ml of 0.1 M sodium oxalate, $Na_2C_2O_4$. Acidify each by adding about 1 ml (20 drops) of 2 M H_2SO_4 (prepared in Part Ia).

(1) Place two of the test tubes in a hot water bath (40–50°C) so that both will be at the same temperature. To one of these test tubes add 5 drops of 0.1 M manganous sulfate, $MnSO_4$. Next add 2 drops of 0.1 M $KMnO_4$ to each of the two test tubes. Shake each test tube to mix, and note the time of reaction for each to reach the same end products.

(2) To *one* of the other two test tubes, at room temperature, add 5 drops of 0.1 M manganous sulfate, $MnSO_4$. Then to each of these two test tubes add 2 drops of 0.1 M $KMnO_4$. Shake each test tube to mix, and compare the time of reaction for each as in (1) above.

b. Label five test tubes 1, 2, 3, 4, 5. In 1 put 5 ml of 6 M hydrochloric acid, HCl; in 2 put 5 ml of 6 M acetic acid (CH_3COOH); in 3 put 5 ml of 1 M HCl; in 4 put 5 ml of 0.1 M HCl; in 5 put 5 ml of 1 M CH_3COOH. To each test tube add a small chip of calcium carbonate, $CaCO_3(s)$. Record the relative rates of reaction observed.

Part IV. (May be demonstrated by the teacher)

a. Heat about $\frac{1}{4}$ ml of powdered lead nitrate, $Pb(NO_3)_2$, in a hard glass test tube. If a reaction occurs, remove the burner and observe what happens. After the material has cooled, reheat it.

b. Place about 1 ml of 0.1 M sodium chloride, NaCl, in a test tube and 1 ml of 0.1 M potassium chromate, K_2CrO_4 in another test tube. Add a few drops of 0.2 M silver nitrate, $AgNO_3$, to each. Note the results. Mix in a test tube about 1 ml of 0.1 M sodium chloride, NaCl, and 1 ml of 0.1 M potassium chromate, K_2CrO_4. Add 0.2 M silver nitrate, $AgNO_3$, one drop at a time, shaking the test tube after the addition of each drop. Continue to add the $AgNO_3$ solution until no further change is observed.

TEACHER'S DEMONSTRATION

Place about $\frac{1}{2}$ ml of ammonium dichromate, $(NH_4)_2Cr_2O_7$, in a crucible and heat it gently. When a reaction starts, remove the burner. Avoid inhaling dust from the reaction.

QUESTIONS

1. In which of the experiments was there no evidence of a chemical reaction?

2. Which chemical reactions produced a new phase?

3. Which reactions in this experiment were exothermic? Which were endothermic?

4. In which reactions did an increase in temperature affect the rate?

5. In which reactions did an increase in concentration affect the rate?

6. In Part IIIa what effect on the rate of the reaction did adding the $MnSO_4$ solution have?

7. What evidence did you observe to indicate that in some of the reactions part of the reactants was not used up?

A Question to Wonder About

Account for the results obtained when solutions of hydrochloric acid and of acetic acid—of the same concentration—reacted with $CaCO_3(s)$.

13

THE HEAT OF REACTION

In this experiment you will use a 250 ml Erlenmeyer flask as the reaction vessel and as a simple calorimeter to measure the heat evolved or absorbed during the reactions.

You may assume that the heat of reaction will be used to change the temperature of the aqueous solution and of the glass of the container. We shall neglect other small losses to the surroundings. Recall that it takes 1.0 calorie to change the temperature of one gram of water one degree Centigrade. It takes 0.2 calorie to change the temperature of one gram of glass one degree Centigrade.

You do not need to weigh the water used since 1.0 ml of water weighs very nearly 1.0 g and you will measure the volume to the nearest milliliter. When the reactants are added to the reaction flask you should note the change in temperature to the nearest 0.2°C. From the change in temperature and the weight of the reactants you can calculate the number of calories evolved or absorbed.

In this experiment you will measure and compare the quantity of the heat involved in three reactions.

Reaction 1. Solid sodium hydroxide dissolves in water to form an aqueous solution of ions:

$$NaOH(s) \longrightarrow Na^+(aq) + OH^-(aq) + x_1 \text{ cal}$$
$$\Delta H_1 = -x_1 \text{ cal}$$

Reaction 2. Solid sodium hydroxide reacts with an aqueous solution of hydrogen chloride to form water and an aqueous solution of sodium chloride:

$$NaOH(s) + H^+(aq) + Cl^-(aq)$$
$$\longrightarrow H_2O + Na^+(aq) + Cl^-(aq) + x_2 \text{ cal}$$
$$\Delta H_2 = -x_2 \text{ cal}$$

Reaction 3. An aqueous solution of sodium hydroxide reacts with an aqueous solution of hydrogen chloride to form water and an aqueous solution of sodium chloride:

$$Na^+(aq) + OH^-(aq) + H^+(aq) + Cl^-(aq)$$
$$\longrightarrow H_2O + Na^+(aq) + Cl^-(aq) + x_3 \text{ cal}$$
$$\Delta H_3 = -x_3 \text{ cal}$$

PROCEDURE

Determination of the Heat of Reaction 1

a. Weigh a clean, dry 250 ml Erlenmeyer flask to the nearest 0.1 g.
b. Put 200 ml (± 1 ml) of cool tap water into the flask. Stir *carefully* with a thermometer until a constant temperature is reached (about room temperature). Record this temperature to the nearest 0.2°C.
c. Weigh about 2 g of solid sodium hydroxide, NaOH, to the nearest 0.01 g. Since sodium hydroxide becomes moist as it is being weighed in the open air, *your teacher will give you special instructions* on weighing rapidly a pre-

scribed number of the solid pellets which will approximate 2 g (between 1.9 g and 2.1 g).
d. Pour the weighed NaOH(s) into the water in the Erlenmeyer flask. Swirl the flask until the sodium hydroxide is dissolved. Place the thermometer into the flask and record the extreme temperature reached.

Before proceeding to *Reaction 2*, rinse the 250 ml flask thoroughly with water. Do not dry.

Determination of the Heat of Reaction 2

Repeat steps *b*, *c*, and *d* used in the determination of the heat for *Reaction 1* except in step *b* substitute 200 ml of 0.25 *M* HCl for tap water.

Rinse the 250 ml flask again and proceed to *Reaction 3*.

Determination of the Heat of Reaction 3

a. Measure 100 ml of 0.50 *M* HCl into the 250 ml flask and 100 ml of 0.50 *M* NaOH into a 250 ml beaker. Both of these solutions should be at, or slightly below, room temperature. Check this with a thermometer. (Rinse and dry the thermometer before transferring it from one solution to another.) Record the temperatures.

b. Add the sodium hydroxide solution to the hydrochloric acid solution. Mix quickly and note the highest temperature reached.

CALCULATIONS

1. *For each reaction*, calculate:

(a) the change in temperature,

(b) the amount of heat that is absorbed by the solution,

(c) the amount of heat absorbed by the flask,

(d) the total amount of heat absorbed,

(e) the number of moles of NaOH used in each reaction,

(f) the total amount of heat involved per mole of NaOH.

2. Express your results as heats of reaction: ΔH_1, ΔH_2, and ΔH_3, all per mole of NaOH.

3. (a) Compare ΔH_2 with $\Delta H_1 + \Delta H_3$ and explain.

(b) Calculate the percent difference between ΔH_2 and $\Delta H_1 + \Delta H_3$ assuming ΔH_2 to be correct.

QUESTIONS

1. Write the net ionic equations for *Reactions 2* and *3*.

2. In *Reaction 1*, ΔH_1 represents the heat of solution of NaOH(s). Look at the net ionic equations for *Reactions 2* and *3* and make a statement concerning the significance of ΔH_2 and ΔH_3.

3. Suppose you had used 4 g of NaOH(s) in *Reaction 1*.

(a) What would be the number of calories evolved?

(b) What effect would this have on your calculation of ΔH_1, the heat involved per mole?

14

A STUDY OF REACTION RATES

To what extent do changes in the concentration of the reacting substances affect the rate of a chemical reaction? Do temperature changes affect the rate of a reaction? In this experiment you will investigate the role of such factors as concentration and temperature by performing some experiments with an interesting reaction called the "clock reaction." You will appreciate the significance of this name after you have completed your first determination.

In order to determine the role of each factor independently you will vary the concentration of one of the reacting species in Part I and vary the temperature in Part II. In each case you will keep other possible variables—"conditions that matter"—constant.

The clock reaction is performed by mixing the two solutions described below.

Solution A is a dilute solution of potassium iodate, KIO_3, which is the source of one of the reacting species, the iodate ion, $IO_3^-(aq)$.

Solution B contains some starch and the other reacting species, the hydrogen sulfite ion, $HSO_3^-(aq)$.

The initial step in the reaction can be represented by the equation

$$IO_3^-(aq) + 3\ HSO_3^-(aq)$$
$$\longrightarrow I^-(aq) + 3\ SO_4^{-2}(aq) + 3\ H^+(aq)$$

When the hydrogen sulfite ions, $HSO_3^-(aq)$, are used up, the iodide ions, $I^-(aq)$, react with the remaining iodate ions, $IO_3^-(aq)$, to produce iodine, $I_2(s)$:

$$5\ I^-(aq) + 6\ H^+(aq) + IO_3^-(aq) \longrightarrow 3\ I_2(s) + 3\ H_2O$$

The molecular iodine forms a blue substance with the starch present in the solution which indicates that the reaction has proceeded to this point.

Part I. The Effect of Concentration Changes

In order to investigate the effect of changing the concentration of one of the reactants on the reaction time you will prepare dilutions of solution A to vary the concentration of the $IO_3^-(aq)$ ion. In each case the concentration of the $HSO_3^-(aq)$ ion will be kept constant and the temperature of all the solutions should be at room temperature. If there is not sufficient time for you to investigate several concentrations, your teacher will assign you and your partner certain concentrations. By exchanging results with other members of the class you will be able to draw some conclusions concerning the effect of this variable.

PROCEDURE

a. Use a clean graduated cylinder to measure 10.0 ml of solution A and pour it into a clean test tube (18 × 150 mm). Rinse the graduated cylinder and in a similar manner place 10.0 ml of solution B into another test tube. If the solutions have been in the laboratory for some time you may assume that they are at room temperature. Otherwise, you should put the test tubes containing the solutions into a 250 ml beaker about two-thirds full of water at room temperature and let them stand for several minutes.

b. Using a watch with a second hand, record the time to the nearest second as you pour solution A into solution B and then pour them back and forth *quickly* three times to obtain uniform mixing. Time should be recorded from the instant both solutions are in contact.

c. Watch the solution in the test tube carefully and record the time again at the first sign of a reaction.

d. Repeat the experiment to check your results if directed to do so by your teacher.

Prepare different concentrations of the KIO_3 solution by diluting solution A as follows. Do as many dilutions as directed by your teacher.

Solution A	Distilled Water
9.0 ml	1.0 ml
8.0 ml	2.0 ml
7.0 ml	3.0 ml
etc.	

Note that the total volume is always 10.0 ml. Mix each of the diluted solutions well.

Repeat the procedure by adding one of the diluted solutions of KIO_3 to 10.0 ml of solution B, both at room temperature.

Calculations and Questions for Part I

1. The concentration of KIO_3 in solution A is 0.02 M. Calculate the number of moles of potassium iodate in each milliliter of solution A.
2. Calculate the initial molar concentration of KIO_3 in each of the mixtures of A plus B prepared in Part I.
3. Why is it important to keep the total volume at 10 ml during the dilutions of solution A?
4. Plot a graph of the concentration–time data with time on the vertical axis (ordinate) and the concentration of the KIO_3 on the horizontal axis (abscissa). Use the data of other members of the class also.
5. What generalizations can you make concerning the effect of varying the concentration on the time of the reaction?
6. How is the time of the reaction related to the rate of the reaction?

Part II. The Effect of Temperature

In order to investigate the effect of changes in temperature you will determine the time of this reaction at room temperature and at other temperatures within a range of $\pm 20°C$ of room temperature. Your teacher will assign particular temperatures for you and your partner to use.

By exchanging results with other members of the class you will be able to draw some conclusions concerning the effect of temperature on the time of reaction.

PROCEDURE

a. Put 10.0 ml of solution A (labeled for Part II) into one test tube (18×150 mm) and 10.0 ml of solution B into another. These solutions must be brought to the desired temperature before they are mixed. Put both test tubes into a 250 ml beaker about two-thirds full of water at the temperature you were assigned to investigate. Let them stand for about ten minutes so the solutions will come to the temperature of the water bath.
b. Using a watch with a second hand, record the time to the nearest second as you pour solution A into solution B and then pour them back and forth *quickly* three times to obtain uniform mixing. Time should be recorded from the instant both solutions are in contact.
c. Place the test tube back in the water bath and observe it carefully. Record the time again at the first sign of a reaction.
d. Repeat the experiment at the same temperature to check your results if directed by your teacher to do so.

Repeat the experiment at another temperature if directed to do so by your teacher.

Calculations and Questions for Part II

1. Plot a graph of the temperature-time data with temperature on the horizontal axis (abscissa) and time on the vertical axis (ordinate).
2. What general relationships can you derive from the above graph?
3. Make a prediction of the time of the reaction at 0°C and at 50°C assuming that the other variables in the experiment are kept constant.

15

CHEMICAL EQUILIBRIUM

In this experiment you will take a quantitative look at the reaction

$$Fe^{+3}(aq) + SCN^-(aq) \rightleftharpoons FeSCN^{+2}(aq)$$

which was presented qualitatively as a class experiment by your teacher. This time you will determine the concentration of each of the ions at equilibrium, and then seek an expression that relates these quantities mathematically in a simple, convenient manner.

The determination of the concentrations will be done colorimetrically. If you have ever looked critically at a glass full of a colored liquid, such as iced tea, you know that the color intensity as viewed through the sides of the glass is much less than the color intensity as viewed from the top down. This is because the color intensity depends upon the concentration of the colored substance *and* on the depth of the solution. Thus, a 1 cm depth of a 1 *M* colored solution will appear to have the same color intensity as a 2 cm depth of a 0.5 *M* solution of the same material. The concentration of two such solutions may be compared by altering their relative depths until the color intensity appears the same. The ratio of the concentrations is found to be the inverse of the ratio of the depths. Note that this procedure gives only relative values for the concentrations. To get absolute values, a standard solution of known concentration must be used.

PROCEDURE

In preparing the standard solution in Step *a* of this experiment, you will use a low, known concentration of thiocyanate ion, $SCN^-(aq)$, and add a large excess of ferric ion, $Fe^{+3}(aq)$. You can assume that essentially all of the thiocyanate ion will be used in forming the complex thiocyanoiron(III) ion, $FeSCN^{+2}(aq)$, and that the equilibrium concentration of the $FeSCN^{+2}(aq)$ ion will be essentially the same as the concentration of the $SCN^-(aq)$ ion with which you started.

Arrange your data sheet so that you can record the depth of the solution in each test tube and the depth of the standard solution compared with each of the other test tubes.

a. Line up five clean test tubes, all of the same diameter, and label them 1, 2, 3, 4, 5. Add 5.0 ml of 0.002 *M* potassium thiocyanate, KSCN, to each of these five test tubes. To test tube 1 add 5.0 ml of 0.2 *M* ferric nitrate, $Fe(NO_3)_3$. This tube will be used as the standard.

b. Measure 10.0 ml of 0.2 *M* $Fe(NO_3)_3$ in your graduated cylinder and fill to the 25.0 ml mark with distilled water. Pour the solution into a clean dry beaker to mix it. Measure 5.0 ml of this solution and pour it into test tube 2. [Save the remainder of the $Fe(NO_3)_3$ solution for Part *c*.] Calculate the concentration of this solution as part of your pre-lab preparation.

c. Pour 10.0 ml of the solution from the beaker into your graduate. Discard the remainder. Continue to fill the graduate to the 25.0 ml mark with distilled water, and pour the solution into a clean dry beaker to mix. Pour 5.0 ml of this solution into test tube 3. Continue dilution in this manner until you have 5.0 ml of successively more dilute solution in each test tube. Calculate the concentration of each of the solutions as part of your pre-lab preparation.

The problem is to compare the solutions in each of the test tubes with the standard tube (number 1) in order to determine the concentration of the thiocyanoiron(III) ion, $FeSCN^{+2}(aq)$.

Wrap a strip of paper around test tubes 1 and 2 to exclude light from the side. Look vertically down through the solutions toward a diffused light source, as shown in Fig. 15-1. If the color intensities appear the same, measure the depth of each solution to the nearest millimeter and record this. If the color intensities do not appear the same, remove some of the solution from the standard tube with a medicine dropper until the color intensities are the same. Put the portion you removed into a clean dry beaker, since you may have to use some of this solution later. In fact, the matching may be accomplished by removing more standard than seems necessary and then replacing part of it drop by drop. When the color intensities are the same in each test tube, measure the depth of both solutions to the nearest millimeter. Repeat the procedure with test tubes 1 and 3, 1 and 4, and finally 1 and 5.

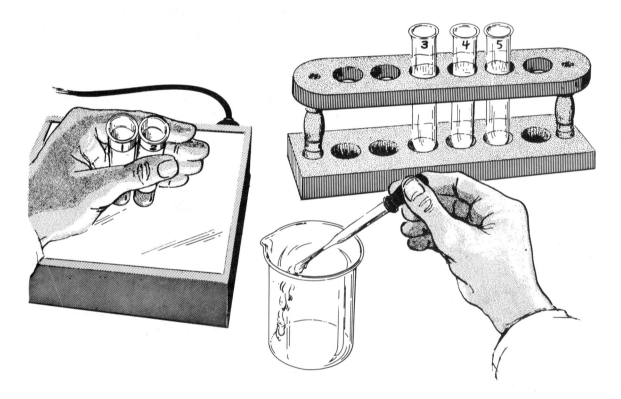

Fig. 15-1. **Comparing the color** *of two samples over a diffuse light source.*

CALCULATIONS

Assume in your calculations that:

(a) the ferric nitrate and the potassium thiocyanate exist in their respective solutions entirely as ions;

(b) in the standard tube (number 1), essentially all the thiocyanate ions have reacted to form thiocyanoiron(III) complex ions. Also remember that *both* solutions are diluted on mixing.

The symbol [ ] will be used to represent the equilibrium concentration in moles per liter. The formula within the brackets denotes the species. Thus the notation $[Fe^{+3}]$ stands for the equilibrium concentration of the ferric ion, Fe^{+3} (aq), in moles per liter.

Do all of the calculations for each test tube 2 through 5 as follows.

1. (a) Calculate the ratio of depths in the color comparison. Example:

$$\text{Ratio} = \frac{\text{Depth of standard matched with tube 2}}{\text{Depth of liquid in tube 2}}$$

(b) From these ratios calculate the equilibrium concentration of thiocyanoiron(III) ion, $[FeSCN^{+2}]$:

$[FeSCN^{+2}]$ = Ratio of depth × conc. of standard

2. From your dilution data calculate the *initial* concentration of $Fe^{+3}(aq)$ ion.

3. Calculate the equilibrium concentration of $Fe^{+3}(aq)$ ion, $[Fe^{+3}]$, by subtracting the equilibrium concentration of the $FeSCN^{+2}(aq)$ ion

from the initial concentration of the $Fe^{+3}(aq)$ ion.

4. Calculate the equilibrium concentration of the $SCN^-(aq)$ ion, $[SCN^-]$, in the same manner as for the $Fe^{+3}(aq)$ ion. Subtract the equilibrium concentration of the $FeSCN^{+2}(aq)$ ion from the initial concentration of the $SCN^-(aq)$ ion.

5. Now try to find some constant numerical relationship between the equilibrium concentrations of the ions in each test tube by multiplying and dividing the values obtained in each test tube in various combinations. For example, for each of the test tubes 2 through 5 calculate:

(a) $[Fe^{+3}] [FeSCN^{+2}] [SCN^-]$;

(b) $\dfrac{[Fe^{+3}] [FeSCN^{+2}]}{[SCN^-]}$;

(c) $\dfrac{[FeSCN^{+2}]}{[Fe^{+3}] [SCN^-]}$.

QUESTIONS

1. Which of the combinations of concentrations, (a), (b), or (c), gives the most constant numerical value? This form is known as the equilibrium constant expression.

2. Restate this expression, in words, using the terms reactants and products.

3. Give a possible explanation as to why such a relationship might exist.

16

DETERMINATION OF THE SOLUBILITY PRODUCT CONSTANT OF SILVER ACETATE, AgCH₃COO

In a saturated solution of a slightly soluble salt in equilibrium with some of the solid, the rate at which ions are leaving the solid crystal is equal to the rate at which they are returning to the crystal:

$$AgCH_3COO(s) \rightleftarrows Ag^+(aq) + CH_3COO^-(aq)$$

The concentrations of the ionic species, silver ions, $Ag^+(aq)$, and acetate ions, $CH_3COO^-(aq)$, determine the equilibrium solubility. The equilibrium constant, called the solubility product constant, is experimentally determined by obtaining the product of the equilibrium concentrations of the ions:

Solubility product constant (K_{sp})
$$= [Ag^+] \times [CH_3COO^-]$$

Note that the "concentration" of the solid silver acetate, $AgCH_3COO(s)$, does not appear in the equilibrium expression since it is not variable.

Since the solubility of a salt varies with the temperature, the solubility product constant is also temperature dependent.

In this experiment you will determine the equilibrium concentration of the silver ions in a saturated solution of silver acetate at room temperature. The reaction utilized is the same as the one used in Experiment 7. Since the acetate ion concentration is the same as the silver ion concentration, you will have the data to calculate the K_{sp}.

PROCEDURE

a. Carefully measure, in a 100 ml graduated cylinder, 100 ml of one of the three samples of saturated silver acetate solutions available. Record its number and the statement of how it was prepared. Pour the solution into a clean, dry 250 ml beaker.

b. Obtain a 30 cm length of 16-gauge copper wire. Clean the surface of the wire with some emery cloth and wind it into a loose coil around a test tube. See Fig. 7-1 for the type of coil desired.

c. Weigh the copper coil to the nearest 0.01 g

and place it into the beaker containing the saturated silver acetate solution. Allow the system to stand overnight so all the silver ions will have an opportunity to react.

d. Shake the silver crystals free from the copper wire into the beaker. Wash the wire in a stream of water from the tap. Rinse it in acetone and when it is dry weigh it.

e. Decant the solution off the silver crystals and rinse them with distilled water. Place the silver into a container designated by your teacher so it can be used again.

CALCULATIONS

1. Calculate the number of moles of Cu(s) which reacted with the silver ions.

2. Recalling the relationship between $Ag^+(aq)$ and Cu(s) obtained in Experiment 7, how many moles of silver ions, $Ag^+(aq)$, were present in the 100 ml sample? What is the concentration of the silver ions in moles per liter?

3. What is the concentration of the acetate ions also present, expressed in moles per liter?

4. Calculate the value of the K_{sp} for silver acetate at room temperature.

5. Compare your results with those of other students who used the other saturated solutions of silver acetate which contained different amounts of the solid, $AgCH_3COO(s)$. What do you conclude about the comparative results?

QUESTIONS AND EXERCISES

1. Propose another method for determining the concentration of $Ag^+(aq)$ in the saturated solution—either using the same experimental method or a different one.

2. If 100 ml of 0.02 M $AgNO_3$ and 100 ml of 0.02 M $NaCH_3COO$ were mixed, would a precipitate be expected to form? Use the average value for the K_{sp} of silver acetate obtained by members of your class in your calculations.

3. Suppose that some solid sodium acetate, $NaCH_3COO$, were added to a saturated solution of silver acetate which is in equilibrium with some $AgCH_3COO(s)$. After the sodium acetate has dissolved, what will be the effect of the increased concentration of the acetate ion on the equilibrium

$$AgCH_3COO(s) \rightleftarrows Ag^+(aq) + CH_3COO^-(aq)$$

4. Calculate the $Ag^+(aq)$ ion concentration if the acetate ion concentration in the solution in Question 3 is 1.0 M. Is this result in agreement with the prediction you made in Question 3?

17

THE HEAT OF SOME ACID–BASE REACTIONS

In Experiment 13 you studied the heat of reaction of a base, sodium hydroxide, NaOH, with hydrochloric acid, HCl. In this experiment you will compare the heat involved when other acids and bases react.

Are all acid–base reactions exothermic? Do some acid-base reactions release more heat per mole of water produced than others? Are all solutions of acids and bases good conductors of electricity (strong electrolytes)? As you carry out this experiment you will be seeking answers to these questions.

PROCEDURE

Your teacher will assign you some specific acid–base combinations to be used. Record your data first in your laboratory notebook and then make it available to the rest of the class, as directed by your teacher.

Use a clean, dry 250 ml beaker as the calorimeter. Obtain 100 ml of each solution in a separate container. Note the initial temperature of each and record it to the nearest 0.2°C. The temperatures of each of the solutions should be at or slightly below room temperature before mixing. (Be sure to rinse and dry your thermometer before transferring it from one solution to another.) Quickly pour both solutions, at the same time, into the beaker calorimeter. Record the highest temperature reached.

The following reactions are to be observed:

(1) 100 ml of 1.0 M HCl and 100 ml of 1.0 M KOH.
(2) 100 ml of 1.0 M CH_3COOH and 100 ml of 1.0 M NaOH.
(3) 100 ml of 1.0 M HNO_3 and 100 ml of 1.0 M NaOH.
(4) 100 ml of 1.0 M HNO_3 and 100 ml of 1.0 M KOH.
(5) 100 ml of 1.0 M CH_3COOH and 100 ml of 1.0 M KOH.
(6) 100 ml of 0.5 M H_2SO_4 and 100 ml of 1.0 M NaOH.

CALCULATIONS

Recall the calculations you made in Experiment 13, reaction (3), to determine the heat involved in producing one mole of water by the reaction

$$H^+ + Cl^- + Na^+ + OH^- = H_2O + Na^+ + Cl^- + heat$$

Make similar calculations of the heat involved

per mole of water produced in each of the reactions performed in this experiment. Record your results and report as directed by your teacher. Include the comparable data on HCl and NaOH from Experiment 13. Neglect the heat used to warm the beaker each time.

DEMONSTRATION OF THE ELECTRICAL CONDUCTIVITY OF SOME ACIDS AND BASES

Before attempting an explanation of the similarities and differences in ΔH values, your teacher will demonstrate the electrical conductivity of each acid and base. Record observations in your notebook, classifying each solution as a good conductor (strong electrolyte) or as a poor conductor (weak electrolyte).

Record your results in the following manner.

(1) Write equations for each of the reactions performed by you and your classmates. Write the formulas for the strong electrolytes in ionic form and the formulas for the weak electrolytes in molecular form to indicate the reacting species present. Include the molar heat for each reaction.

(2) What regularities do you observe about the ΔH values obtained for the reactions involving the various acids and bases? What do all of the equations have in common?

(3) The values of ΔH for the various reactions will be collected and tabulated by your teacher or by a designated member of your class. Study the tabulated results and note the average values for each combination of acid and base.

Make any generalizations possible about the ΔH values the class obtained when strong electrolytes reacted compared with those obtained for reactions which involved a weak electrolyte.

(4) Attempt a theoretical explanation for the differences and similarities in the ΔH values based upon the energy involved in making and breaking chemical bonds.

(5) On the basis of your present knowledge of strong and weak acids, answer the Question to Wonder About at the end of Experiment 12.

18

THE DETERMINATION OF THE HYDROGEN ION CONCENTRATION OF SOLUTIONS USING INDICATORS

Acid–base indicators are dyes whose colors depend upon the hydrogen ion concentration, $[H^+]$, of a solution. There are numerous dyes which are suitable for this purpose and each one changes color over a particular range of hydrogen ion concentration. You are already familiar with one dye, litmus, which is red when the $[H^+] = 10^{-6} M$ or greater and blue when the $[H^+] = 10^{-8} M$ or less.

For this experiment you will use two indicators which have color changes in the acid range, methyl orange and orange IV, and two indicators for the basic range, indigo carmine and alizarin yellow R.

You will first make up a series of standard solutions with known concentration of $H^+(aq)$ in the acid range by diluting a solution of a strong acid, 0.1 M HCl. In a similar manner you will prepare a series of solutions in the basic range by diluting a solution of a base, 0.1 M NaOH. These prepared solutions will serve as standards. Using appropriate indicators, you will be able to determine the $[H^+]$ of an "unknown" solution by comparing the color of the unknown solution with the color of the standard solutions. You will also determine the hydrogen ion concentration of a solution of a weak acid and calculate its equilibrium constant. Finally you will use an indicator to compare the volume of 0.1 M NaOH required to react with equal volumes of 0.1 M HCl and 0.1 M acetic acid, CH_3COOH.

PROCEDURE

You will work in pairs in performing this experiment. Student A will prepare the standard solutions in the acid range and Student B will do the same for the basic range. Label the test tubes so that each of you can use the standards to determine the $[H^+]$ of an "unknown" solution in Part III. You may work as partners on Parts IV and V but each of you should keep individual data sheets.

Part I. The Preparation of Standard Solutions in the Acid Range: $[H^+] = 10^{-1} M$ to $10^{-4} M$

STUDENT A

a. Obtain about 5 ml of 0.1 M HCl in a clean, dry 13 × 100 mm test tube. Label this test tube $[H^+] = 0.1 M$. Since hydrochloric acid is a strong acid it can be assumed to be completely ionized in this dilute solution.

b. Prepare some 0.01 M HCl by diluting one volume of 0.1 M HCl with nine volumes of distilled water. Use a calibrated pipette or medicine dropper such as you prepared in Experiment 10 (see Fig. 10-2). An appropriate volume to use would be 0.5 ml of 0.1 M HCl and 4.5 ml of distilled water. Thoroughly mix this solution and label it $[H^+] = 0.01 M$ or $10^{-2} M$.

c. In a similar manner prepare 5 ml of 0.001 M HCl by diluting some of the standard solution prepared in step b. Mix it thoroughly and label it $[H^+] = 0.001 M$ or $10^{-3} M$.

d. Finally prepare 5 ml of 0.0001 M HCl by diluting some of the standard solution prepared in step c. Mix it thoroughly and label it $[H^+] = 0.0001 M$ or $10^{-4} M$.

e. Pour half of each of the standard solutions into clean test tubes so you will have two sets of standards. Label the new test tubes to correspond with each standard. For one set add one drop of the orange IV solution to each of the four test tubes. For the other set add one drop of methyl orange solution to each test tube.

f. Make a table for recording the colors observed in each of the solutions for the various [H+]. Retain these standards for Parts III and IV.

Part II. The Preparation of Standard Solutions in the Basic Range: [OH−] = 10⁻¹ M to 10⁻⁴ M

STUDENT B

Follow the directions of Part I*a*, *b*, *c*, *d* except to prepare the solutions in the basic range use 0.1 *M* NaOH instead of 0.1 *M* HCl.

Since sodium hydroxide is a strong electrolyte, a dilute solution of NaOH can be considered to be completely ionized so the hydroxide ion concentration of 0.1 *M* NaOH is 0.1 *M* or 10⁻¹ *M*.

Label the solutions prepared in Parts II*b*, *c*, and *d*, [OH−] = 10⁻² *M*, [OH−] = 10⁻³ *M* and [OH−] = 10⁻⁴ *M*, respectively.

e. Divide the solutions to obtain two sets of the four standards as outlined in Part I*e*. For one set add one drop of the indigo carmine solution to each of the four test tubes and to the other set add one drop of alizarin yellow R solution to each test tube.

f. Make a table for recording the colors observed in each of the solutions for the various [H+]. Retain these standards for use in Part III.

Part III. The Determination of the Hydrogen Ion Concentration of an "Unknown" Aqueous Solution (To be done individually)

a. Obtain about 5 ml of an "unknown" solution from your teacher in a clean, dry test tube. Test a portion of it with litmus paper to determine whether the [H+] is in the range greater than 10⁻⁷ *M* or lower than 10⁻⁷ *M*.

b. Place about 2 ml of the "unknown" solution into each of two small test tubes. If the solution is in the acid range, add a drop of orange IV solution to one test tube and a drop of methyl orange to the other test tube. If the

solution is in the basic range, use the indicators indigo carmine and alizarin yellow R, respectively.

c. Compare the colors with those of the standards prepared by either you or your partner. Record the hydrogen ion concentration of the "unknown" solution.

Part IV. The Determination of the Hydrogen Ion Concentration of a Solution of a Weak Acid: Acetic Acid, CH₃COOH

a. Obtain about 5 ml of a solution of acetic acid in a small, clean, dry test tube. Note and record the concentration. Some students will use a 0.1 *M* solution and others will use a 1.0 *M* solution.

b. Place about 2 ml of the acetic acid solution assigned to you into each of two small, clean, test tubes. Add a drop of orange IV solution to one test tube, a drop of methyl orange solution to the other.

c. Compare the colors with those of the standards containing the same indicators and estimate the [H+] of the acetic acid solution as accurately as you can. Record the H+(*aq*) concentration and use this to calculate the equilibrium constant of acetic acid.

Part V. The Determination of the Volume of 0.1 M NaOH Required to React with Equal Volumes of 0.1 M HCl and of 0.1 M CH₃COOH.

a. Use your clean calibrated medicine dropper (Fig. 10-2) to measure out 1.0 ml of 0.1 *M* HCl into a clean small test tube.

b. Rinse the medicine dropper thoroughly and measure out 1.0 ml of 0.1 *M* CH₃COOH into another test tube.

c. Add a drop of the indicator solution phenolphthalein to each test tube. Phenolphthalein is a dye which is colorless in the range where the [H+] = 10⁻¹ *M* to 10⁻⁹ *M* but turns pink when the [H+] is less than 10⁻⁹ *M* (also [OH−] = 10⁻⁵ *M*).

d. Rinse the medicine dropper thoroughly and fill it with 0.1 *M* NaOH. Add this solution of base, drop by drop, to each acid solution until the indicator turns to a pink color which does not disappear on mixing the solution in the test tube. Record the number of drops of 0.1 *M* NaOH required in each case.

CALCULATIONS

Calculate the equilibrium constant for the equilibrium involving the aqueous solution of the weak acid, acetic acid, CH_3COOH:

$$CH_3COOH \rightleftharpoons H^+(aq) + CH_3COO^-(aq)$$

Use the value for $[H^+]$ determined in Part IVc.

You may assume that the concentration of the acetate ion, $[CH_3COO^-]$, is equal to the $[H^+]$ and that the concentration of acetic acid, CH_3COOH, is essentially the concentration of the solution you used, 0.1 M or 1 M.

QUESTIONS

1. Predict qualitatively the effect of each of the following experiments on the above equilibrium.

   (a) Some of the salt, sodium acetate which produces the ions $Na^+(aq)$ and $CH_3COO^-(aq)$, is dissolved in the 0.1 M acetic acid solution. Would the $[H^+]$ increase or decrease?
   (b) Some sodium hydroxide solution is added, drop by drop, to the 0.1 M CH_3COOH.

2. How do you explain the results noted in Part V, where you compared the volume of 0.1 M NaOH required to react with equal volumes of 0.1 M HCl and 0.1 M CH_3COOH?

3. The $H^+(aq)$ concentration of a 1 M solution of benzoic acid is 8×10^{-3} M.

   (a) What percent of the benzoic acid, C_6H_5COOH, is ionized in this aqueous solution?
   (b) Predict what volume of 1 M NaOH would be required to react with 10ml of 1 M C_6H_5COOH.

Assume that the reaction will be carried to the point where phenolphthalein turns pink, as in Part V.

Optional Questions

1. Calculate the $H^+(aq)$ concentration of each of the solutions prepared in Parts IIa, b, c, and d. Use the relation $[H^+][OH^-] = 10^{-14}$.

2. The pH of a solution is a shorthand way of designating the hydrogen ion concentration, $[H^+]$. For example, when the $[H^+] = 0.1$ M or 10^{-1} M the pH is 1. Note that the pH is simply the exponent to which 10 is raised (the logarithm) with the sign changed. What is the pH of each of the standard solutions prepared in Parts Ia, b, c, and d and Parts IIa, b, c, and d?

3. What is the pH of your "unknown" solution?

19

APPLYING LE CHATELIER'S PRINCIPLE TO SOME REVERSIBLE CHEMICAL REACTIONS

Most of the chemical reactions you have observed in the laboratory seem to have gone to completion—that is, all the reactants appear to have been used up to form the products. Actually, *all* chemical reactions are reversible, even though the extent of reversibility may sometimes be very small. In many reactions which you will encounter from now on in the laboratory you must concern yourself with their reversibility and the possibilities of controlling the extent of reversibility.

In this experiment you will study some reactions where appreciable reversibility is found and the presence of the reactants and products can be readily observed by noting color changes or the formation of a precipitate. In an aqueous solution the chromate ion, $CrO_4^{-2}(aq)$, can be converted to the dichromate ion, $Cr_2O_7^{-2}(aq)$, and conversely, the $Cr_2O_7^{-2}(aq)$ ion can be converted to the $CrO_4^{-2}(aq)$ ion. The extent to which these reactions take place is dependent upon the concentration of the hydrogen ion, $H^+(aq)$, in the solution. The $H^+(aq)$ concentration can be increased by adding a source of $H^+(aq)$-hydrochloric acid, HCl. The $H^+(aq)$ concentration can be decreased by adding a solution of sodium hydroxide, NaOH, which contains the hydroxide ion, $OH^-(aq)$. The $OH^-(aq)$ reacts with $H^+(aq)$ to form H_2O.

PROCEDURE

Part I. The Chromate Ion, $CrO_4^{-2}(aq)$ – Dichromate Ion, $Cr_2O_7^{-2}(aq)$, Equilibrium

a. Obtain about 5 ml of 0.1 M potassium chromate, K_2CrO_4, and 5 ml of 0.1 M potassium dichromate, $K_2Cr_2O_7$, in separate test tubes. These solutions will serve as sources for the ions, $CrO_4^{-2}(aq)$ and $Cr_2O_7^{-2}(aq)$. Record the color of each solution.

b. Place 10 drops (about 0.5 ml) of each solution into separate 13 × 100 mm test tubes. Add, a drop at a time, some dilute sodium hydroxide, 1 M NaOH, alternately to each solution until a color change is noted in one of the tubes. Record the colors now. Retain these tubes for Step *e*.

c. Repeat the procedure of Step *b* with fresh solutions in clean test tubes except add dilute hydrochloric acid, 1 M HCl, drop by drop, alternately to each test tube. Record the color change observed. Retain these test tubes for Step *d*.

d. Add 1 M NaOH, drop by drop, to one of the tubes obtained in Step *c* until a change is noted.

e. Add 1 M HCl, drop by drop, to one of the tubes obtained in Step *b* until a change is noted.

Questions for Part I

1. What can you conclude about the reaction $2\ CrO_4^{-2}(aq) \longrightarrow Cr_2O_7^{-2}(aq)$ and its dependence on hydrogen ions, $H^+(aq)$, as noted in Steps *c* and *e*? Balance this equation by adding the proper number of $H^+(aq)$ ions and H_2O molecules to the appropriate side of the equation.
2. What can you conclude about the reverse reaction $Cr_2O_7^{-2}(aq) \longrightarrow 2\ CrO_4^{-2}(aq)$ and its dependence on hydroxide ions, $OH^-(aq)$, as noted in Steps *b* and *d*? Balance the equation by adding the proper number of $OH^-(aq)$ ions and H_2O molecules to the appropriate side of the equation.

Part II. The Equilibrium of Solid Barium Chromate, BaCrO₄(s) with a Saturated Solution of Its Ions:

$$BaCrO_4(s) \rightleftharpoons Ba^{+2}(aq) + CrO_4^{-2}(aq)$$

a. Place 10 drops (about 0.5 ml) of 0.1 M K_2CrO_4 in a clean test tube. Add 2 drops of 1 M NaOH. Add, a drop at a time, 0.1 M barium nitrate, $Ba(NO_3)_2$, until a change is noted. Record the result. Retain this test tube for Step c.

b. Place 10 drops (about 0.5 ml) of 0.1 M $K_2Cr_2O_7$ in a clean test tube. Add 2 drops of 1 M HCl then 10 drops of 0.1 M $Ba(NO_3)_2$. Record the result. Retain this test tube for Step d. Record your conclusions about the relative solubilities of $BaCrO_4(s)$ and $BaCr_2O_7(s)$ from your observations in Steps a and b.

c. To the test tube from Step a add, drop by drop, 1 M HCl until a change is noted. Record your observation.

d. To the test tube from Step b add, drop by drop, 1 M NaOH until a change is noted. Record your observation.

e. Suggest a way to reverse the changes and reactions you observed in Step c. Do the same for Step d. Try these experiments.

f. Place 10 drops (about 0.5 ml) of 0.1 M $K_2Cr_2O_7$ in one test tube and the same amount of 0.1 M K_2CrO_4 in another test tube. Add a few drops of 0.1 M $Ba(NO_3)_2$ to each. Note the result and record the observation.

Questions for Part II

1. From your observation in Step f, what can you conclude about the relative equilibrium concentrations of $CrO_4^{-2}(aq)$ ion in each of the solutions 0.1 M $K_2Cr_2O_7$ and 0.1 M K_2CrO_4?

2. Use the equations you balanced in questions 1 and 2 of Part I to explain the results you obtained in Steps c, d, and e of Part II.

3. Make a statement summarizing your results with the chromate ion-dichromate ion equilibrium which includes the application of the Principle of Le Chatelier.

Part III

Repeat Parts Ia, b, and c using the solutions of $K_2Cr_2O_7$ and K_2CrO_4 but testing each with several drops of dilute solutions of each of the following substances: CH_3COOH, HNO_3, $Ca(OH)_2$, H_2SO_4, KOH, C_2H_5OH, NH_3. Record any changes in color noted.

Questions for Part III

1. (a) Which substances in solution caused the color to change from that of the $Cr_2O_7^{-2}(aq)$ ion to that of the $CrO_4^{-2}(aq)$ ion?
   (b) Which substances in solution caused the reverse color change?

2. What ionic species do the solutions you listed in 1a have in common? Answer the same question for the solutions listed in 1b.

3. Give an explanation of the results you noted

   (a) When ethyl alcohol, C_2H_5OH, was added.
   (b) When the solution of aqueous ammonia, $NH_3(aq)$, was added.

4. On the basis of your conclusion made in question 2, predict some additional substances which in solution might have the same effect on the CrO_4^{-2}–$Cr_2O_7^{-2}$ equilibrium as those you categorized in questions 1a and 1b.

20

AN INTRODUCTION TO OXIDATION-REDUCTION

In Experiment 7 you observed the reaction in which copper metal was oxidized to cupric ions by the silver ions, which were in turn reduced to silver metal. In this case there was a transfer of electrons from Cu(s) to Ag$^+(aq)$. The Cu(s) is the reducing agent or the substance which reduced the Ag$^+(aq)$ ion. The Ag$^+(aq)$ ion is the oxidizing agent or the substance which oxidized the Cu(s).

$$Cu(s) \rightleftarrows Cu^{+2}(aq) + 2\ e^-$$

$$\frac{2\ e^- + 2\ Ag^+(aq) \rightleftarrows 2\ Ag(s)}{2\ Ag^+(aq) + Cu(s) \rightleftarrows 2\ Ag(s) + Cu^{+2}(aq)}$$

In Part I of this experiment you will observe some possible oxidation–reduction reactions involving several metals and metallic ions. Upon analysis of your results you can then determine the relative strengths of the metals as reducing agents (tendency to lose electrons) and of the metallic ions as oxidizing agents (tendency to gain electrons).

In Part II you will make a similar comparison of the relative oxidizing strength of three non-metallic elements in column 7: chlorine, bromine, and iodine. In this case you will determine which halogen, Cl_2, Br_2, or I_2 is capable of removing electrons from which of the halide ions, Cl^-, Br^-, and I^- and thus arrange the halide ion–halogen element half-reactions, $2\ X^- \longrightarrow X_2 + 2\ e^-$, in order of decreasing ease of oxidation.

PROCEDURE

Part I

a. Obtain small, clean strips or pieces of the metals zinc, Zn, copper, Cu, and lead, Pb. Also have available the following solutions: 0.1 M $Zn(NO_3)_2$; 0.1 M $Cu(NO_3)_2$; 0.1 M $Pb(NO_3)_2$.

b. Observe possible reactions of each of the metals in each of the solutions. For each combination use 3 ml of the solution in a 13 × 100 mm test tube and a small, freshly cleaned piece of metal.

c. Record the cases where a reaction occurred.

Part II

PRELIMINARY OBSERVATIONS

a. In separate test tubes, obtain about 3 ml of the three halogens in solution: in the first,

chlorine in water, $Cl_2(aq)$; in the second, bromine in water, $Br_2(aq)$; in the third, iodine in water containing a little ethanol (I_2 is only very slightly soluble in water).

b. Add about 1 ml of carbon tetrachloride, CCl_4, to each. Fit with a stopper then shake each test tube for about 15 seconds. Note the color of the carbon tetrachloride phase which contains the dissolved halogen.

TESTS FOR SPONTANEOUS
OXIDATION-REDUCTION REACTIONS

c. Put about 3 ml of 0.1 M NaBr in one test tube and about 3 ml of 0.1 M NaI in another test tube. To each test tube add 1 ml of carbon tetrachloride. Add 1 ml of a fresh solution of chlorine in water to each and stopper and shake the test tube for about 15 seconds. Note the color of the carbon tetrachloride phase and compare with the preliminary tests in *a* and *b* of Part II.

d. Repeat the test outlined in Step *c*, except use 0.1 *M* NaCl and 0.1 *M* NaI. Add 1 ml CCl$_4$ and about five drops of bromine water to each. Shake the test tubes as directed above.

Record your results.

e. Repeat the test outlined in Step *c*, except use 0.1 *M* NaCl and 0.1 *M* NaBr. Add 1 ml CCl$_4$ and five drops of the iodine solution to each. Shake the test tubes as directed before. Record your results.

CONCLUSIONS AND QUESTIONS

1. Which of the metals tested was oxidized by both of the solutions of the other metallic ions? Which one was oxidized by only one of the metallic ions? Which one was oxidized by neither of the other metallic ions.

2. Arrange the metal–metal ion half-reactions M(s) $\rightleftharpoons$ M^{+2}(aq) + 2 e^- in a column in order of decreasing ease of oxidation. Since you know from Experiment 7 that Cu(s) was oxidized by Ag$^+$(aq), add the Ag(s) $\rightleftharpoons$ Ag$^+$(aq) + e^- half-reaction to your list in the appropriate place.

3. Write balanced total reactions for the cases where oxidation-reduction reactions between metals and metallic ions were observed [see the example for Cu(s) and Ag$^+$(aq) in the introductory section of this experiment].

4. Which of the halide ions tested was oxidized by both of the other halogen elements? Which halide ion was oxidized by only one halogen element? Which halide ion was not oxidized by any of the halogen elements used?

5. Arrange the halide ion–halogen element half-reactions in a column in order of decreasing ease of oxidation.

6. Write balanced total reactions for the cases where oxidation-reduction reactions occurred between halide ions and elementary halogens.

7. Use the additional information given below to construct a series of all seven half-reactions discussed in this experiment in order of decreasing ease of oxidation.

   (a) Ag$^+$(aq) is a stronger oxidizing agent than is I$_2$(s) but is a weaker one than Br$_2$(l).
   (b) I$^-$(aq) is a weaker reducing agent than is Cu(s) but is a stronger one than Ag(s).

8. Would it be feasible to store a solution of copper sulfate in a container made of metallic zinc? Of metallic silver? Give reasons for your answers.

9. Would you expect jewelry made of an alloy of silver and copper to tarnish (oxidize) in a laboratory where fumes of bromine are present? Explain.

21

ELECTROCHEMICAL CELLS

This study of simple cells will be performed by small groups of students operating as a team. If the number of high resistance voltmeters available is limited, your teacher will perform the experiment on the lecture table. In either case, you are to record the data and be as critical in your considerations as though you were doing the experiment by yourself.

In Experiment 20 you made a study of the ease of oxidation of several metals by the ions of other metals. This qualitative study provided a means by which you could deduce which of these metal-metal ion combinations produced a spontaneous reaction. In this experiment you will construct various cells which will utilize spontaneous oxidation-reduction reactions in such a way that the

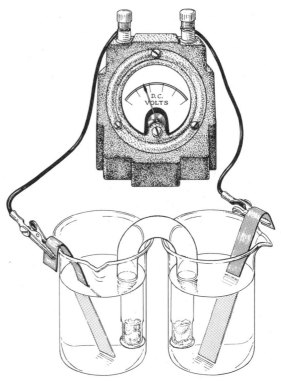

Fig. 21-2. **A cell** *using a U-tube as a salt bridge.*

electrons are transferred through a wire rather than by actual contact of the oxidizing agent with the reducing agent. See Fig. 21-1. The oxidation half-reaction takes place at the electrode (anode) in one half-cell and the reduction half-reaction takes place at the electrode (cathode) in the other half-cell. When the two half-cells (porous cup and beaker in Fig. 21-1) are placed together such that their solutions are in contact, a cell is produced whose voltage is a quantitative measure of the tendency of the chemical reaction in the cell to take place. The two half-cells may also be two beakers whose solutions are connected with a salt bridge—a large U-tube containing a solution of an electrolyte such as $NH_4^+(aq)\ NO_3^-(aq)$ —as shown in Fig. 21-2.

Study the procedure carefully and prepare a suitable data table before coming to the lab.

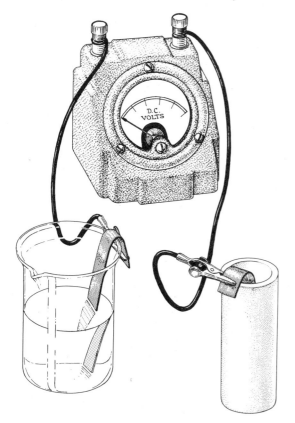

Fig. 21-1. **Assembling an electrochemical** *cell using a porous cup.*

PROCEDURE

Part I. A Cell Using the Half Cells Zn(s)–Zn^{+2} (0.5 M) and Cu(s)–Cu^{+2} (0.5 M)

a. Add 0.5 M copper nitrate, Cu(NO$_3$)$_2$, to the porous cup until it is about half full. Place a clean strip of copper in the cup. Connect the copper electrode to the positive terminal of the voltmeter.
b. Add 0.5 M zinc nitrate, Zn(NO$_3$)$_2$, to the 250 ml beaker until it is about half full. Place a clean strip of zinc in the beaker. Connect the zinc electrode to the negative terminal of the voltmeter.
c. Note the voltage reading with the half-cells in the position shown in Fig. 21-1.
d. Place the porous cup in the beaker. Note the voltage reading. Remove the porous cup and retain both half-cells for use in other combinations.

Part II. A Cell Using the Half-Cells Ag(s)–Ag$^+$ (0.5 M) and Cu(s)–Cu^{+2} (0.5 M)

Prepare a silver—0.5 M silver nitrate half-cell in a clean beaker. Place the porous cup containing the Cu(s)–Cu^{+2} (0.5 M) in the beaker and note the voltage. Which electrode should be attached to the negative terminal of the voltmeter?

Part III. A Cell Using the Half-Cells Pb(s)–Pb^{+2} (0.5 M) and Cu(s)–Cu^{+2}(0.5 M)

Set up this cell as before, placing the lead–0.5 M lead nitrate solution in a clean beaker. Place the porous cup containing the Cu(s)–Cu^{+2} (0.5 M) in the beaker and note the voltage.

Part IV

Use other combinations of half-cells as directed by your teacher, if time permits. Do not contaminate the solutions in the half-cells since they can be used by students in other classes during the day.

Part V. Effect of Concentration of the Oxidizing Agent. (Teacher Demonstration)

a. Reconstruct the cell in Part I, except place the Cu(s)–Cu^{+2} (0.5 M) solution in the beaker and the Zn(s)–Zn^{+2} (0.5 M) solution in the porous cup, and note the voltage again.
b. Add to the beaker, with stirring, about half as much 2 M sodium sulfide, Na$_2$S, as there is copper nitrate solution. Note the voltmeter reading and the appearance of the solution in the beaker.

CONCLUSIONS AND QUESTIONS

1. (a) Will the cell operate when arranged as in Figure 21-1? Explain why.
   (b) What is the purpose of the porous cup (or salt bridge)?
2. (a) What is the spontaneous half-reaction taking place in the
       (i) Zn(s)–Zn^{+2}(0.5 M) half-cell?
       (ii) Cu(s)–Cu^{+2}(0.5 M) half-cell?
   (b) Write the total reaction.
3. (a) What is the direction of electron flow in the wire connecting the zinc and copper electrodes?
   (b) What is the direction of the flow of negative ions through the porous cup (or salt bridge)?
4. Predict the $E°$ for the cell using the half-cells Zn(s)–Zn^{+2} (0.5 M) and Cu(s)–Cu^{+2} (0.5 M). Use the oxidation potentials in Appendix 8. How did

your experimental results compare with the calculated value?

5. What is your explanation of the results obtained when sodium sulfide solution was added to the Cu(s)–Cu^{+2}(0.5 M) half-cell?

6. (a) Make a sketch of a cell which uses the half reaction Zn(s)–Zn^{+2} (0.5 M) as one electrode and the half reaction Br$^-$(0.5 M)–Br$_2$(l) into which an inert electrode is placed. Predict the direction of electron flow through the wire connecting the zinc and inert metal electrodes. Predict the potential of the cell. Write the equation for each electrode reaction and for the total cell reaction.
   (b) Heat is evolved as zinc reacts with bromine. Would the potential of this cell be greater or smaller if the cell were heated? Explain.

22

REACTIONS BETWEEN IONS IN SOLUTION

The solubility table in Appendix 10 permits you to predict which ions in aqueous solutions combine to produce a precipitate of a slightly soluble compound. The oxidation-reduction table in Appendix 8 compares the relative strengths of oxidizing and reducing agents and permits you to predict when certain ionic species in solution will undergo an oxidation-reduction reaction. Remember that predictions based on $E°$ values show only which is favored, the reactants or the products, after *equilibrium* is reached. They do not predict the rate of the reaction. (See the Textbook, Section 12-2.3.) In cases where the reaction you predicted does not occur immediately, make observations again, later in the period or the next day before you evaluate your predictions.

In Part I of this experiment you are to predict, before coming to the laboratory, whether an appreciable reaction will take place when each of the ten combinations of solutions of ions are mixed. If you predict that a reaction will take place, write a balanced equation for it in your laboratory notebook. Use ions where appropriate, and label precipitates with *(s)* and gases with *(g)*.

Check your predictions by performing the experiments in the laboratory. Include those for which you predicted no reaction. Do not be biased by your predictions; record what you actually observe.

In Part II you need not make preliminary predictions. These reactions are somewhat more complex. Record your observations as you perform the experiments, and later attempt to explain the results. Write balanced ionic equations for the reactions you can interpret correctly.

PROCEDURE

Part I. Predict the Results—then Try the Reaction

For each trial use about 3 ml portions of each solution and mix thoroughly in a 13 × 100 mm test tube unless directed otherwise.

a. 0.1 M magnesium nitrate, $Mg(NO_3)_2$, and 0.1 M sodium hydroxide, NaOH.

b. 0.1 M magnesium nitrate, $Mg(NO_3)_2$, and 0.1 M sodium sulfate, Na_2SO_4.

c. Saturated (about 0.1 M) barium hydroxide, $Ba(OH)_2$, and 0.1 M sulfuric acid, H_2SO_4.

d. 0.1 M potassium dichromate, $K_2Cr_2O_7$, and 0.1 M sodium sulfite, Na_2SO_3, acidified with 1 drop of 6 M H_2SO_4.

e. 0.05 M potassium permanganate, $KMnO_4$, and 1.0 M hydrochloric acid, HCl.

f. 0.1 M potassium iodide, KI, and 0.1 M ferric chloride, $FeCl_3$.

   Add about 1 ml (20 drops) of CCl_4 to the mixture and shake the test tube. This makes it easier to detect the presence of any halogen, owing to its greater solubility in the CCl_4 phase. Recall the solubility of iodine in CCl_4 in Part II of Experiment 20.

g. 0.1 M potassium bromide, KBr, and 0.1 M ferric chloride, $FeCl_3$.

   Add 1 ml CCl_4 and shake the test tube.

h. 0.1 M ferrous sulfate, $FeSO_4$, acidified with 3 drops of 6 M H_2SO_4, and 0.01 M potassium permanganate, $KMnO_4$.

i. 0.1 M zinc sulfate, $ZnSO_4$, and 0.1 M ammonium carbonate, $(NH_4)_2CO_3$.

j. Saturated (about 0.1 M) barium hydroxide, Ba(OH)$_2$, and 0.1 M zinc sulfate, ZnSO$_4$.

Part II (Optional)

The following reactions are more complex than those in Part I. You are not expected to make predictions. Do the experiment, make careful observations, and later attempt to interpret the results. Write ionic equations for the reactions you can interpret.

     Experiments k through n are a series involving reactions of hydrogen peroxide and some ions of chromium in an acid or basic solution.

     Use 3 ml of each solution and mix thoroughly.

k. 0.1 M chromium sulfate, Cr$_2$(SO$_4$)$_3$, acidified with 3 drops of 6 M H$_2$SO$_4$, and 3% hydrogen peroxide.

l. 0.1 M chromium sulfate, Cr$_2$(SO$_4$)$_3$, to which 6 M NaOH is added dropwise until the precipitate Cr(OH)$_3$ first formed just redissolves and the Cr(OH)$_4^-$ ion is produced, and 3% hydrogen peroxide.

m. 0.1 M potassium dichromate, K$_2$Cr$_2$O$_7$ acidified with 3 drops of 6 M H$_2$SO$_4$, and 3% hy-

drogen peroxide.

n. 0.1 M potassium dichromate, K$_2$Cr$_2$O$_7$, to which 6 M NaOH is added dropwise until the solution turns yellow, and 3% hydrogen peroxide.

     Experiments o through q are a series involving reactions of the lead ion with various anions.

o. 3 ml of 0.1 M lead nitrate, Pb(NO$_3$)$_2$, and 3 ml of 1.0 M sodium chloride NaCl.

     Allow the precipitate to settle a few minutes and decant about 3 ml of the supernatant liquid from the residue for use in experiment p. Some of the precipitate can be present in the decanted liquid; the liquid does not have to be clear.

p. 3 ml of the decanted liquid from experiment o and 3 ml of 0.1 M potassium iodide, KI.

     Allow the precipitate to settle and decant the supernatant liquid from the residue for use in experiment q. Some of the precipitate can be present in the decanted liquid; the liquid does not have to be clear.

q. 3 ml of the decanted liquid from experiment p and 3 ml of 0.1 M sodium sulfide, Na$_2$S.

23

QUANTITATIVE TITRATION

Relative amounts of reactants and products of a reaction are commonly investigated in two ways in the laboratory: gravimetrically (by weight), as in Experiments 6 through 9, and volumetrically (by volume and concentration) as in this experiment. Titration is the name given to the process of determining the volume of a solution needed to react with a given weight, or volume, of a sample. We shall use this process to study quantitatively the reaction between an acid and a base.

A common reaction in water solution is that of the hydrogen ion of an acid with the hydroxide ion of a base to form water. Recall the use of indicators in the determination of the hydrogen ion concentration (Experiment 18). Phenolphthalein will be used as the indicator in this experiment since its color change occurs when the same number of moles of acid and base have been added. This point in the reaction is called the **endpoint.**

PROCEDURE

Using hydrochloric acid of known concentration, you will first standardize a sodium hydroxide solution, that is, determine its concentration expressed as moles per liter. Using this standard base you will then titrate a known weight of an unknown solid acid, and then calculate the number of grams of this acid that will react with one mole of the base. After this experimental value has been determined, your teacher will tell you the formula of the acid. You will then write the equation for the reaction and calculate the value for the number of grams of acid that will react with one mole of the base and compare it with your experimental value.

Part I. Standardization of the Solution of a Base

a. Obtain two burets. See the section on the care of burets at the end of this experiment. Clean the burets and rinse one with 10 ml of the standard hydrochloric acid. Rinse the other with 10 ml of the sodium hydroxide solution you are *instructed to use*. If there are not enough burets for each student, your teacher will demonstrate how to use a pipet to measure the volume of acid. After rinsing the bu-

rets, fill the first with the standard acid and the second with the base. See Fig. 23-2.

b. Record the volume in each buret by reading the bottom of each meniscus to the nearest 0.1 ml. Let about 10 ml of hydrochloric acid flow into a clean 250 ml Erlenmeyer flask. Add about 15 ml of distilled water and 3 drops of phenolphthalein.

c. Hold the neck of the Erlenmeyer flask with one hand and manipulate the buret with the other. As you add the sodium hydroxide, gently swirl the flask so the solutions will become mixed. Continue adding sodium hydroxide until the first faint pink color develops. If the color disappears upon mixing the solution, add more sodium hydroxide, drop by drop, until a persistent pink color is obtained. If you go beyond this endpoint you may add a few drops of acid, and then complete the titration with a few more drops of sodium hydroxide. (Take care not to go beyond the last calibration marks on the buret.) Record the volume reading at the bottom of the meniscus of each buret. Rinse the Erlenmeyer flask thoroughly before repeating the titration.

d. Refill the burets with the proper solutions and

perform at least one more titration. If directed by your teacher, repeat until you obtain ratios of volume of acid to volume of base which agree to 1 or 2%.

Part II. Titration of an Unknown Acid

a. Obtain a solid unknown acid from your teacher. Weigh the vial or test tube containing the sample to the nearest ± 0.01 g. Remove a suitable amount, (about one gram, or as directed by your teacher) of the solid acid into a clean flask as shown in Fig. 23-1 and weigh the vial and contents again. Dissolve the sample in 50 ml of distilled water and add 3 drops of phenolphthalein. If all of the acid does not dissolve at this point, it will dissolve later during the titration when the acid will be converted to the more soluble sodium salt.

b. Refill the proper buret with some of the solution of base used previously and record the initial reading. Add the base to the acid solution until the first persistent, faint pink color appears. Be careful not to overrun the endpoint. If you pass the endpoint, add a little more of the solid acid and reweigh the vial. Be sure to include the weight of any solid acid added to the weight of your sample. Retitrate to the endpoint and record the final buret reading.

c. Repeat the titration with a similar sample. Use the knowledge you gained in the first titration. That is, assuming you used 40 ml of base to titrate a certain weight of acid, and that you have almost the same weight of acid for the second trial, you can run 35 ml of base into the flask rapidly and complete the last part of the titration cautiously.

Part III. Optional Titration

If time permits, you may bring from home commercially available household acidic or basic substances to titrate with either your standard acid or base. Examples of items readily available are lemon juice, vinegar, household ammonia, washing powders. Determinations which are possible are the percent acetic acid, CH_3COOH, in vinegar; the percent citric acid, $C_6H_8O_7$, in lemon juice; the percent ammonia, NH_3, in household

ammonia. Your teacher will tell you how large a sample to use and which indicator is appropriate.

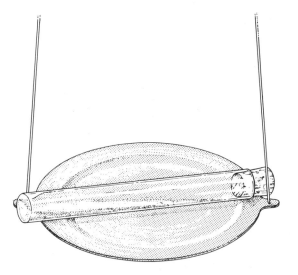

Fig. 23-1. **Weighing a sample** *and transferring it to a flask.*

CALCULATIONS

1. From the concentration given and volume used, calculate the number of moles of hydrochloric acid involved in each titration of Part I.

Example: If 10 ml of 0.05 *M* HCl is used, the number of moles involved in the reaction is obtained as follows:

$$\frac{10 \text{ ml}}{1000 \text{ ml/liter}} \times \frac{0.05 \text{ mole}}{\text{liter}} = 0.0005 \text{ mole}$$

2. From the equation for the reaction, how many moles of base are used per mole of acid in Part I?

3. Using the relationship in question 2, calculate the moles of base used.

4. Calculate the molarity of the base.

5. From the weight of the solid acid and the volumes involved in its titration, calculate the weight of the solid unknown acid that will react with one mole of the base.

6. Using the formula of the acid given you by your teacher and the equation for the reaction, calculate the theoretical value for the weight of the acid that will react with one mole of the base.

7. Determine the percentage error, using the value calculated in question 6 as the accepted value. (See Appendix 4.)

CARE OF BURETS

Cleaning

Place a few milliliters of a detergent solution into a buret, then use a buret brush to clean the inside surface. Rinse well, first with tap water and then with distilled water. After draining the buret, note if there are any droplets still adhering to the sides of the tube. If there are, the glass is not thoroughly cleaned and should be rewashed. When glass is clean, water wets it evenly.

Preparing for Use

After cleaning a buret, add 5–10 ml of the solution that is to be used in that buret. Let several milliliters of solution flow through the tip. Turn the buret to a horizontal position and with a rotary motion, slowly pour the rest of the solution out of the top. Make sure that the solution wets the inside completely. For a more complete rinsing, repeat the above.

Fill the buret to the top with the solution to be used. Permit air bubbles in the tip to escape by turning the tip upward as shown in Fig. 23-2. Let solution flow from the tip until the bottom of the meniscus is at zero or below.

If a drop hangs on the tip before you start a titration, discard it by touching it to a beaker (see Fig. 23-2). However, a drop formed *during* a titration must be caught by touching it to the side of the container being used and rinsing it into the container with distilled water.

Reading the Volume

When reading the volume on the buret, be sure to have your eye level with the bottom of the meniscus and read the volume carefully at the bottom of the curve (see Fig. 9-3). In each titration use an absolute minimum of 10 ml of each solution to attain a precision of 1%.

After Use

Drain and rinse the buret several times with tap water, then, as a final rinse, use distilled water. Glass reacts with basic solutions so take special care in rinsing a buret that has had such solutions in it. A rinse with dilute acid after one water rinse will help assure that the base is removed. Follow this with the water rinses described above.

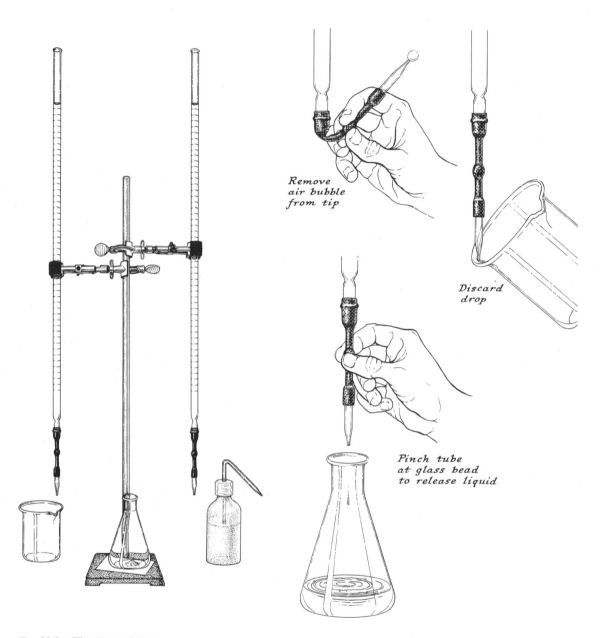

Remove
air bubble
from tip

Discard
drop

Pinch tube
at glass bead
to release liquid

Fig. 23-2. **Titration techniques.**

24

CONSTRUCTION OF A LOGICAL MODEL

In Chapter 1 of the Textbook your attention was first called to the basic activities of science:

to accumulate information through observation,

to organize this information and to seek regularities in it,

to wonder why the regularities exist,

to communicate the findings to others.

Up to this point in the course you have not been deeply concerned with the third item—wondering why the regularities exist. However, in Chapters 14–17, great emphasis will be placed on this activity. There, current theoretical explanations and models will be presented in order that you can see how scientists account for the observed regularities and principles you have studied earlier. The explanations involve atoms, electrons, and the molecules formed by chemical bonds between atoms. None of these can be directly observed and any properties assigned to them must be inferred by interpreting experiments giving visible results.

An analogous situation might be the attempt to determine the nature of an object contained inside a sealed container by making a series of external observations. In the present experiment you will be given a sealed box which contains an object. Without opening the box, make all the observations you can by carefully shaking, tilting, or otherwise manipulating it. Obtain data which will enable you to make closer and closer approximations of the size, shape, and some of the physical properties of the object. The goal is not to guess what specific object the box contains, but to describe it sufficiently that you can make a drawing or model of its general appearance.

Record the observations made each time a given manipulation of the box has been performed. Draw conclusions based on these observations. Test your conclusions by devising other experiments. Use these observations to strengthen or modify your first conclusions. Repeat this process until your description of the object is as detailed as you can make it.

List some additional experiments you would like to perform but for which the necessary equipment is not available to you. What information would you hope to get from these experiments?

25

THE RELATION BETWEEN THE MOLES OF COPPER, MOLES OF SILVER, AND MOLES OF ELECTRONS INVOLVED DURING ELECTROLYSIS

Michael Faraday was the first person to determine the relationship between the number of electrons flowing through a circuit during electrolysis and the weight of the products at the electrodes. In this experiment we shall repeat some of his measurements.

Figure 25-1 shows the details of the electric circuit and the cells we shall use. The source of electrons, which we might call an "electron pump," is either a battery or another suitable source of direct current which is constructed such that the electrons are "pumped" in one direction. The ammeter measures the rate of flow of electrons passing through the circuit in a given unit of time. We shall use a unit based on moles of electrons: one ampere is that amount of current flowing when 1.04×10^{-5} moles of electrons pass through any cross-section of the conductor in a one second interval of time. Since electric charge does not build up in any part of the circuit, the current must be the same in all sections of the circuit.

The source of direct current, the "electron pump," causes the electrons to be crowded onto one terminal or electrode and to be drained away from the other. The circuit is complete when at one electrode an ion or molecule in the electrolyte solution accepts electrons and is reduced, while at the other electrode an ion or molecule loses electrons and is oxidized. The electrode at which reduction occurs is the cathode and that at which oxidation occurs is the anode.

Using the materials and circuitry shown in Fig. 25-1, determine the relationship between the number of moles of electrons flowing during the experiment, the number of moles of copper atoms reduced and oxidized, and the number of moles of silver atoms reduced.

PROCEDURE

a. Obtain a cylinder of copper screen to be used as the cathode and a sheet of copper wound into a spiral, or a heavy copper wire wound into a tight coil, to serve as the anode. Handle the electrodes by the connecting wires only. Otherwise, your fingers may leave grease marks upon which the copper deposit will not adhere well.

b. Obtain a cylinder of copper screen which has a thin coating of silver to be used as the cathode and a strip of lead which will serve as the anode in the silver plating cell. Do not touch the clean electrodes with your fingers.

c. Weigh each of the clean, dry cathodes (screen cylinders) to the nearest 0.01 g.

d. Suspend the electrodes in separate 250 ml beakers by attaching them to a wooden holder or by clamping them with clothespins as directed by your teacher. Be sure that the anodes are centered within the cylindrical cathodes and that the electrodes do not touch each other.

e. Make all of the connections in the circuit as shown in Fig. 25-1, except leave one of the wires to the variable resistor disconnected. Adjust the variable resistor so that its full resistance will be utilized. Ask your teacher to check your setup.

f. Add the electrolyte solution containing the copper ions to the beaker with the copper anode. Use enough to just cover the copper screen cathode.

g. In a similar manner add the silver plating solution to the other beaker.

h. Make the last connection and *quickly* adjust the current to 1 ampere by decreasing the resistance being used in the variable resistor. Record the time to the nearest second.

i. Let the current flow for 30 minutes. Watch the ammeter and keep the current as close to 1

ampere as possible by adjusting the variable resistor.

j. Record the time to the nearest second as you disconnect one of the wires to break the circuit. Rinse the two cathodes by gently dipping each into a beaker containing some cold water. Do not agitate the electrodes so vigorously that the metal deposits are dislodged.

k. Rinse the cathodes with acetone to remove the water droplets. Allow them to dry by evaporation (about 2 or 3 minutes).

l. When thoroughly dry, weigh each of the cathodes to the nearest 0.01 g on the same balance you used before.

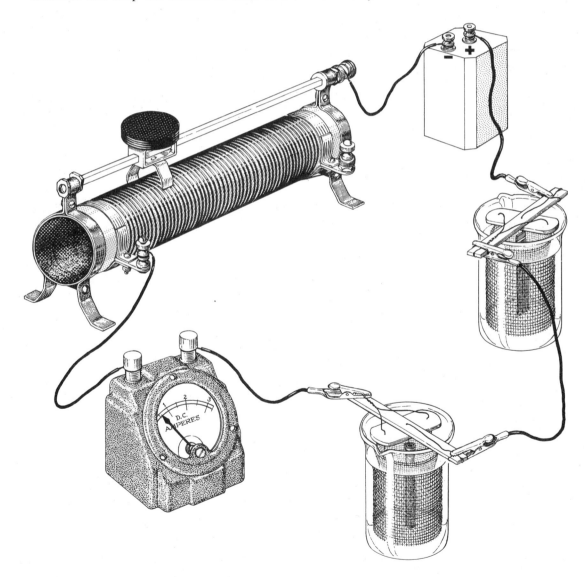

Fig. 25-1. **Two electrolytic cells** *in a series circuit.*

CALCULATIONS AND QUESTIONS

1. Calculate the number of moles of electrons which were used. Recall that 1.04×10^{-5} mole of electrons are involved when a current of one ampere flows for one second.

2. Calculate the number of moles of copper deposited on the cathode from the electrolyte containing copper ions.

3. Calculate the number of moles of silver deposited on the cathode from the electrolyte containing silver ions.

4. Calculate the relationship between moles of electrons and moles of copper reduced.

5. Calculate the relationship between moles of electrons and moles of silver reduced.

6. Write equations for the cathode reactions. Assume that the reacting species are simple copper ions or silver ions.

7. Calculate the relationship between moles of silver reduced and moles of copper reduced.

8. How does this relationship compare to the relationship you obtained in Experiment 7?

9. Write the balanced equation for the oxidation reaction which occurs at the copper anode. How would you expect the loss of weight at the copper anode to compare with the gain of weight at the cathode?

10. What are some sources of error in your measurements and procedures? How many significant figures in the mole relationship can be justified by your data?

11. How many moles of electrons would be required to plate 52.0 g of chromium on a cathode from a suitable cell containing an electrolyte solution in which the chromium is in oxidation state (VI)?

26

INVESTIGATION OF SOME OF THE PROPERTIES OF A PAIR OF *CIS-TRANS* ISOMERS

Maleic acid and fumaric acid have the same molecular formula: $C_4H_4O_4$. Each contains two carboxyl, —COOH, groups and each exhibits the properties of an unsaturated organic compound which indicates the presence of a double bond,

$$\begin{array}{c}\diagdown \quad \diagup \\ C{=}C \\ \diagup \quad \diagdown \end{array}$$. Yet each possesses its own distinctive

properties, such as melting point, solubility, density, and stability. Chemists attribute these differences to the geometry, or arrangement in space, of the atoms in the molecule. Observe the space filling and the ball and stick molecular models of the two acids illustrated in Fig. 26-1 and note that in the *trans-* form the carboxyl groups are on opposite sides of the molecule and in the *cis-* form they are on the same side. The fact that the two forms can be isolated indicates that rotation of the molecule at the double bond does not occur readily.

In this experiment you will convert some maleic acid to fumaric acid by heating it in an

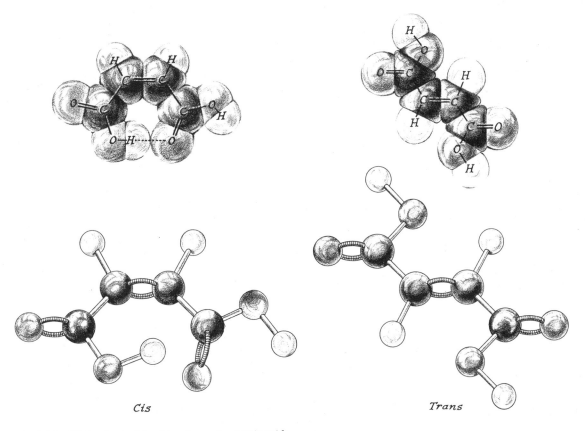

Cis

Trans

Fig. 26-1. **Molecular models** *of two isomeric organic acids.*

aqueous solution containing some hydrochloric acid. The hydrochloric acid is not used up by the reaction but serves merely as a source of H+ which is the catalyst. You will be able to determine the completeness of the conversion by comparing the weight of the fumaric acid obtained with that of the maleic acid initially used. You will also compare some of the properties of each acid and attempt to explain any differences in terms of their structure. This should enable you to make some arguments as to which acid, maleic or fumaric, is the *trans-* form and which is the *cis-* form.

PROCEDURE

Part I. Conversion of Maleic Acid to Fumaric Acid

a. Weigh 6.0 g of maleic acid in a clean, dry 100 ml beaker. Add 10 ml of distilled water and warm slightly to dissolve the acid.

b. Add 15 ml of 12 *M* HCl and cover the beaker with a watch glass. Place the beaker inside a 250 ml beaker which is about one-third full of water. Heat this water bath to boiling for about 5 minutes or until a solid material forms in the smaller beaker.

c. Cool the solution to room temperature by placing the smaller beaker in a cold water bath.

d. Pour the mixture into a filter. Wash any remaining solid into the filter by rinsing the beaker with small amounts of cold water from a wash bottle. Allow the crystals to drain. If an aspirator is available, attach its hose to the stem of the funnel to draw out the wash water remaining in the funnel. Turn the water on cautiously to avoid breaking the filter paper.

e. Transfer the crystals to a weighed watch glass.

f. Dry the crystals by placing the watch glass over an appropriate sized beaker about one-third full of boiling water.

g. When the sample is dry, weigh it on the watch glass. Label the sample "Fumaric Acid."

Part II. Comparison of the Two Isomers

a. Compare the solubility of the two acids by placing 1.0 ± 0.1 g of each into separate 18 × 150 mm test tubes, properly labeled. Add 10 ml of distilled water to each and make a qualitative comparison of solubility.

b. Compare the melting points of the acids using the setup shown in Fig. 26-2. See Appendix 2, Fig. 2-4, for method of inserting thermometer into a rubber stopper.

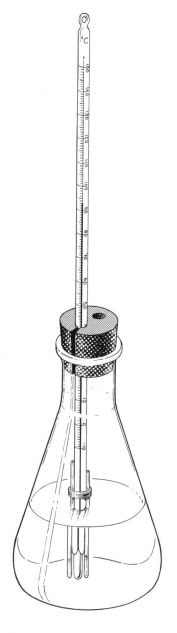

Fig. 26-2. **A melting point apparatus.**

(1) Obtain two capillary melting point tubes (1.0–1.5 mm diameter and 6–12 cm long). Make one tube shorter than the other by cutting off a centimeter or so. Seal one end of each tube in a burner flame. Place maleic acid in the shorter tube to identify it.

(2) Push the open end of the shorter capillary tube into some *dry* maleic acid. Tap the closed end gently on the table so the solid packs down into the tube. Continue to do this until the depth of solid is one or two centimeters. Similarly fill the longer tube with a sample of *dry* fumaric acid.

(3) Attach the tubes to a −10 to 150°C thermometer with a small rubber circle cut from the end of a piece of rubber tubing. See Fig. 26-2. The liquid in the flask is vegetable oil.

(4) Clamp the melting point apparatus in place and heat it gradually with a low burner flame. Move the flame occasionally to achieve more uniform heating of the oil bath. Heat slowly and watch the capillary tubes closely as the temperature approaches 120°C. At the sign of first melting of either solid record the temperature. **Caution:** *Do not exceed the 150°C limit of the thermometer.* The melting point of the other sample is 287°C.

c. Compare the chemical properties of the two isomers as follows:

(1) Prepare a solution of maleic acid by adding approximately 0.1 g to about 20 ml of distilled water. Divide the solution among three small test tubes. Estimate the hydrogen ion concentration by testing one portion with a few drops of Orange IV. To another portion add a 3 cm strip of magnesium ribbon. Record the results. To another portion add a small amount (size of a pea) of sodium carbonate. Record the results.

(2) Repeat the above tests, using fumaric acid. Record the results and compare them with those obtained with maleic acid.

(3) (To be assigned to selected students or demonstrated by the teacher.) Titrate a 1.00 ± 0.01 g sample of each acid with a standard base solution using phenolphthalein as the indicator. Refer to Experiment 23 for directions for carrying out the titrations.

Results

Record all results in a systematic manner to show clearly the differences and similarities in properties of the two acids.

QUESTIONS

1. Assuming that equilibrium concentrations were achieved in Part I, which acid would you classify as the more stable with respect to the transformation of one into the other?

2. What does each of the following experiments contribute to your knowledge of the structure of each isomer?

   (a) The reactions with magnesium and with sodium carbonate.
   (b) The titration data, that is, the number of moles of base required to titrate each acid.
   (c) The reactions of solutions of each acid with an indicator.

   (d) The melting point determination.

3. Maleic acid can lose a molecule of water from each molecule of acid when its two carboxyl groups react to form an anhydride. Which structural isomer, *cis-* or *trans-*, do you predict it is? Fumaric acid cannot do this. Explain.

A Question to Wonder About

Compare the molecular models of the *cis-* and *trans-* isomers. Considering their structure, attempt to account for observed differences in solubility and melting point.

27

THE PACKING OF ATOMS OR IONS IN CRYSTALS

The solid state of matter nearly always consists of a regular arrangement of atoms, molecules, or ions. If we represent each building block as a point, then the crystal structure can be represented by a regularly repeating pattern called the space lattice. In this experiment we shall use styrofoam spheres as the building blocks and we shall study some of the ways they can be packed to form some typical metallic crystals. Three types of packing will be investigated: hexagonal closest packing, face-centered cubic packing (also called cubic closest), and body-centered cubic packing. We shall observe the number of nearest neighbors (the coordination number) of the particles in each of these structures.

In addition, we shall investigate some of the possibilities of packing spheres of different radii into lattices which represent ionic crystals. The importance of the ratio of the radii of the cations and anions as it determines the coordination number will be observed by building the rock salt lattice, $Na^+Cl^-(s)$, and the Wurtzite lattice, $Zn^{+2}S^{-2}(s)$.

PROCEDURE

Secure a supply of styrofoam spheres of the following diameters: 36 2-inch, 13 1-inch, and 13 $\frac{3}{4}$-inch. Short lengths of pipestem cleaners can be used to connect the spheres.

Part I. Some General Considerations on Packing of Spheres

a. Determine how many 2-inch spheres you can pack around a marked single sphere in the same plane. Do you think this number is dependent on the size of the sphere? Check your prediction.

b. Place additional loose spheres above and below the marked sphere so that they all touch it. How many nearest neighbors does it have? In other words, what is the coordination number for this type of closest packing?

c. Note that the three spheres in the top layer can occupy a position directly above the comparable bottom layer or they may be twisted through an angle of 60° and still have the same coordination number.

Part II. Model A—Hexagonal Closest Packing

a. Connect the groups of spheres you used in Part I with short lengths of pipestem cleaners to obtain the layers shown in Fig. 27-1.

b. Place the layer of 3 spheres on the desk with the apex of the triangle facing you.

c. Now place the layer of 7 spheres over the 3 spheres such that the center sphere fits closely into the depression of the first layer.

d. For the top layer, place another layer of 3 spheres over the center sphere of the second layer such that they are oriented directly over

Fig. 27-1. **Layers for hexagonal closest packing.**

those in the first layer. If a pattern such as this were expanded into space until billions of atoms were involved, one would have a model of a very small crystal of metallic magnesium, zinc, and many other metals. Note the coordination number. Retain this model for use in Part IV.

Part III. Model B—Cubic Closest Packing or Face-centered Cubic Packing

a. Construct the layers illustrated in Fig. 27-2 using 2-inch spheres and pipestem cleaners as before.

b. Place the first layer flat on the desk. Place the second layer on it such that the spheres rest in the spaces between the corner spheres of the first layer. Now add the third layer such that its spheres are directly over those in the first layer. Study this model carefully. Why is it called face-centered cubic? This is the packing which is found in copper, silver, aluminum, and many other metals.

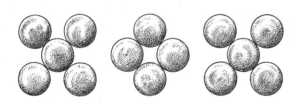

Fig. 27-2. **Layers for cubic closest packing.**

Part IV. Comparison of Hexagonal Closest Packing with Cubic Closest Packing

a. Return to the hexagonal closest packing Model A. Arrange it such that the top layer is not directly over the first layer but is rotated at 60° with respect to it.

b. Rotate this model slightly and look for 4 spheres forming a square facing you. Now take the top layer off of Model B and place it on the 4 spheres you located on Model A. Note that this new model contains a face-centered cube, just like Model B but tilted toward you.

c. In the light of the above comparison, is there a difference in coordination number in the two types of closest packing? Is there a difference in density when spheres of comparable size and weight are involved in each of these types of packing? Most metals crystallize in only one, not both, of these forms. What does this indicate about the directional nature of bonds between atoms of these metals?

Part V. Model C—Body-centered Cubic Packing

a. Construct the layers shown in Fig. 27-3 using 2-inch spheres. Be sure to leave space of about $\frac{1}{4}$ inch between the spheres as indicated.

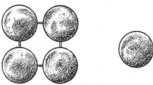

Fig. 27-3. **Layers for body-centered cubic packing.**

b. Place the single sphere in the center of the first layer and then place the third layer such that its spheres are directly over the first layer. Study the symmetry of this model and justify its name. This type of packing is typical of the alkali metals, such elements as sodium and potassium. Can you suggest any reason in terms of numbers of valence electrons that Na and K crystallize in this form, while most of the other metals crystallize in a close-packed form?

c. Metallic iron crystallizes in the body-centered cubic form called α-ferrite below 906°C. Above this temperature the stable form is γ-ferrite, which is face-centered cubic. At 1401°C the crystal form changes back to a body-centered cubic solid called δ-ferrite. What is the coordination number of iron in each of these forms? Can you suggest any reason in terms of numbers of available bonding electrons for these transitions?

Part VI. The Sodium Chloride Lattice

a. Ionic crystals are formed by packing positive and negative ions alternately into a lattice. Sodium ions have a diameter of 1.90Å while that of the chloride ions is 3.62Å. We shall use 1-inch spheres for Na⁺ and 2-inch spheres for Cl⁻ in our model, and thus approximate their relative sizes.

b. Use Model B with its 2-inch spheres for the face-centered cubic arrangement of the chloride ions. Now insert the 13 1-inch spheres, representing sodium ions, into the holes between the chloride ions in each layer. Note that the Na^+Cl^- lattice is an interpenetrating set of face-centered cubes—one involving Na^+ and one Cl^-.

c. What type of ion surrounds each Na^+? Each Cl^-? What is the coordination number of the spheres representing Na^+, and of those representing Cl^-?

d. Note that in order to achieve this type of lattice there must be a favorable relation between the relative radii of the two spheres which will permit a given sphere to fit into a given hole in the lattice. What is the radius ratio for Na^+/Cl^- ions? Can you account for the stability of this type of packing in terms of interionic forces?

Part VII. The Zinc Sulfide (Wurtzite) Lattice

a. Since the zinc ion has a diameter of 1.5 Å and the diameter of the sulfide ion is 3.7 Å, we shall use $\frac{3}{4}$-inch spheres for the Zn^{+2} ion and 2-inch spheres for the S^{-2} ion to approximate the relative sizes.

b. Use Model A with its hexagonal closest packing orientation to represent the lattice of the larger sulfide, S^{-2}, ions. Attach one of the smaller $\frac{3}{4}$-inch spheres, representing the zinc ions, Zn^{+2}, directly above each of the larger spheres in each of the three layers of Model A. (Use short lengths of pipestem cleaners or toothpicks.)

Place the large layer on the table top with the small spheres pointed down. Place one of the small layers on the large layer in such a way that the smaller spheres fit into alternate depressions. Invert the two layers and place the other small layer, with small spheres pointing up, above the larger layer so that each sphere on the top layer is directly above a sphere on the bottom layer.

c. What is the coordination number of the spheres representing Zn^{+2} ions?

d. What is the radius ratio of zinc ions to sulfide ions?

QUESTIONS

1. Write a brief description of each type of packing of metallic crystals that you studied.

2. Answer all questions raised in the Procedure sections. Label them by Parts and Sections; for example, Q. I-a.

3. In one of the types of cubic packing, the spheres occupy about two-thirds of the space and in the other they fill about three-fourths of the space available. Identify which type is which. Which is more dense? Which has the larger number of bonds?

4. From your consideration of the models constructed in Parts VI and VII, what relation can you deduce concerning the radius ratio of ions and the coordination number in crystals? In which case is the number of interionic attractions the greater around any given ion?

5. Suppose you have a crystal XY with the sodium chloride packing in which each of the ions is the same size as the Na^+ and Cl^- respectively but each is doubly charged X^{+2} and Y^{-2}. Would XY have a higher or lower melting point than NaCl? Suggest a real pair of crystals which meet the above criteria and look up their melting points to check your prediction.

6. Suppose you have a crystal AB with the sodium chloride packing in which each of the ions has the same charge A^+ and B^- as Na^+ and Cl^- but the radii of A and B are proportionately larger. Would AB have a higher or lower melting point than NaCl? Suggest a real pair of crystals that meets the above criteria and look up their melting points to check your prediction.

28

SOME REACTIONS OF HYDROCARBONS AND OF ALCOHOLS

In the first part of this experiment you will investigate the reactivity of some examples of different classes of **hydrocarbons**—compounds containing carbon and hydrogen only. You will use cyclohexane, C_6H_{12}, as an example of a saturated hydrocarbon with a cyclic structure; cyclohexene, C_6H_{10}, as the example of an unsaturated cyclic hydrocarbon; and benzene, C_6H_6, and toluene, $C_6H_5CH_3$, as examples of aromatic hydrocarbons. You will investigate the relative ease of oxidation of these compounds by a strong oxidizing agent, an alkaline solution of potassium permanganate. You will also compare their ability to add or substitute bromine when treated with a solution of bromine, Br_2, in carbon tetrachloride.

In the second part of the experiment you will investigate some of the reactions of **alcohols**—compounds of carbon and hydrogen which contain the functional group —OH. Examples of alcohols which you will use are: methanol, CH_3OH, ethanol, C_2H_5OH, and three isomeric alcohols with the formula C_4H_9OH. The names and more detailed formulas of the latter three alcohols are:

1-butanol, $CH_3CH_2CH_2CH_2OH$,

a primary alcohol;

2-butanol, $CH_3CH_2CHOHCH_3$,

a secondary alcohol;

2-methyl-2-propanol, $CH_3COH(CH_3)CH_3$,

a tertiary alcohol.

PROCEDURE

Before beginning the experiment, examine carefully ball-and-stick models of the various hydrocarbons and alcohols listed in the introductory section. Draw detailed structural formulas for each compound. See the Textbook, Figs. 18-8 and 18-12, for examples of structural formulas for related compounds.

Read the experimental procedure and prepare suitable tables for recording your results.

Part I. Reactions of Hydrocarbons

a. Label a clean, dry 13 × 100 mm test tube for each of the hydrocarbons to be tested: cyclohexane, cyclohexene, benzene, and toluene. Add about 10 drops of the appropriate hydrocarbon to each test tube. Prepare about 4 ml

of a 0.005 M alkaline potassium permanganate solution by adding 2 ml of 0.01 M $KMnO_4$ to 2 ml of 6 M NaOH. Add 20 drops (about 1 ml) of this solution to each of the test tubes containing the different hydrocarbons. Place a cork stopper in each test tube and shake the contents gently to obtain more intimate contact between the two phases. Note any changes in the color of the aqueous layer after about one minute. Shake the contents occasionally and observe the tubes after five minutes.

b. Place about 10 drops of each hydrocarbon into four properly labeled, small test tubes. Add about 20 drops (about 1 ml), of 0.1 M Br_2 in carbon tetrachloride, drop by drop, to each of the test tubes. Place a stopper in each tube and shake the contents occasionally as you add the bromine solution and note any changes in color. Continue the addition of the bromine to those hydrocarbons where a change is noted until the bromine color persists.

Part II. Some Reactions of Alcohols

a. The reaction of ethanol, C_2H_5OH, with neutral, acidic, and basic solutions of potassium permanganate.

Place about 2 ml of 0.01 M $KMnO_4$ in each of three small test tubes. Add 2 ml of distilled water to one, 2 ml of 6 M H_2SO_4 to the second, and 2 ml of 6 M NaOH to the third. Label them neutral, acidic, and basic $KMnO_4$. Now add 2 drops of C_2H_5OH to each, shake the contents, and note any changes in the color of the permanganate solutions. Add another drop or two of ethanol and observe any further changes which may take place after five minutes. Note any differences in the rate of oxidation as well as in the reaction products. (*Note:* The color of a solution containing the manganate ion, MnO_4^{-2}, is green, manganese dioxide, MnO_2, is a brown precipitate, and a solution containing the manganous ion, Mn^{+2}, is very light pink, almost colorless.)

b. The reaction of methanol, CH_3OH, with hot copper oxide.

Place 2 ml of methanol in a small test tube. Make a small spiral of bare copper wire by winding several turns of 22-gauge wire around the point of your pencil. Leave about 15 cm of straight wire to serve as a handle. Hold the coil of the wire in the burner flame until it is red hot. Thrust the hot wire into the test tube so the coil is just above the level of the CH_3OH. Note the change in the appearance of the copper coil. Cautiously smell the vapors in the test tube and compare them with those of methanol. The new substance formed is formaldehyde, HCHO, which you may recognize as the liquid used to preserve specimens in the biology laboratory.

Optional: An alternate method for carrying out the above reaction—one which illustrates the exothermic nature of the reaction—may be demonstrated by your teacher.

Wrap a penny (or a comparable size piece of copper screen) with a few turns of heavy copper wire so that it can be suspended above about 10 ml of methanol in a small beaker. Place a glass stirring rod across the beaker and hook the wire over it such that the penny is suspended about 1 cm above the surface of the methanol. Remove the penny or copper screen to a flame well away from the beaker and heat to a dull red heat. Quickly suspend the hot penny above the methanol in the beaker and note the interesting cyclical reaction that occurs.

c. Comparison of some reactions of three isomeric alcohols with the formula C_4H_9OH.

(1) Reaction with metallic sodium. (May be demonstrated by your teacher as an option.)

Place about 1 ml of 1-butanol in a small test tube. Ask your teacher to supervise the addition of several thin slices of freshly cut metallic sodium. Note any reaction that occurs.

Repeat this test with the other two isomeric alcohols.

(2) Reaction with concentrated hydrochloric acid. (*Note:* This reagent is used to compare the ease with which the —OH group of the alcohol R—OH reacts with 12 M HCl to form H_2O and the alkyl chloride, R—Cl. The alkyl halide is only slightly soluble in the aqueous phase and its presence is shown by a cloudiness due to the suspension of droplets.)

Place about 1 ml of 1-butanol in a small test tube. Add about 5 ml of 12 M HCl. Stopper the test tube, shake the mixture, and after a minute look for the presence of the slightly soluble alkyl chloride.

Repeat this test with the other two isomeric alcohols.

(3) Reaction with a neutral solution of 0.01 M $KMnO_4$.

Place about 2 ml of 0.01 M $KMnO_4$ solution in a small test tube. Add an equal volume of 1-butanol, stopper the test tube, and shake the contents. Observe the color of the permanganate solution over a period of five minutes with occasional shaking.

Repeat this test with the other two isomeric alcohols.

QUESTIONS AND EXERCISES

1. Examine the ball-and-stick models of the various hydrocarbons you tested. Which contain double bonds? Which of the models is (are) planar, which nonplanar? Is there an alternate structure for cyclohexane?

2. (a) Which of the hydrocarbons were readily oxidized by the alkaline solution of $KMnO_4$?
   (b) Which was reactive with the bromine solution?
   (c) What is the relationship between the reactivity noted in *a* and *b* and the structure of the hydrocarbons.

3. Write the balanced equation for the reaction in which methanol was oxidized by the hot copper oxide.

4. What differences were noted when C_2H_5OH reduced the neutral, acidic, and basic solutions of $KMnO_4$? Assuming that C_2H_5OH was oxidized to acetic acid, CH_3COOH, in each case, write balanced equations for each reaction. Be sure to use the reduction half-reaction which involves the reduction product of manganese which you observed.

5. In the reactions involving the three isomeric alcohols with the formula C_4H_9OH, what did each of the following tests show about the functional group $-OH$ and its position in each alcohol?

   (a) The test with metallic sodium.
   (b) The test with concentrated hydrochloric acid.
   (c) The test with neutral potassium permanganate.

6. Write a balanced equation for each case in Question 5*a*, *b*, and *c*, where a reaction occurred.

7. Examine the ball-and-stick models of the three isomeric alcohols with the formula C_4H_9OH. Note especially any difference in the nature of the carbon to which the functional group $-OH$ is attached. Discuss the relation of your results as summarized in Question 5 to the structure of the three alcohols.

8. *Optional:* Note the physical properties of the three alcohols summarized in the following table:

Alcohol	m.p. (°C)	b.p. (°C)	Solubility in g/100g water
1-butanol	−89	117.7	7.9
2-butanol	−89	100	12.5
2-methyl-2-propanol	25.5	82.8	infinitely soluble

Using principles discussed in Chapter 17 of the Textbook, The Bonding in Liquids and Solids, discuss the relationship of the structure of the three alcohols and the trends and differences in the physical properties tabulated.

9. *Optional:* There is a fourth alcohol with the formula C_4H_9OH. Draw a structural formula for it and name it. How would you predict that it would react with

   (a) metallic sodium;
   (b) 12 *M* HCl;
   (c) neutral 0.01 *M* $KMnO_4$?

29

THE PREPARATION OF SOME DERIVATIVES OF ORGANIC ACIDS

Organic acids may be represented by the structural formula R—C with the O double-bonded and OH, in which the R stands for an organic radical such as CH_3, C_2H_5, or C_6H_5. The carboxyl group, —COOH, is the functional group which all organic acids have in common. Various acid derivatives involve substitutions in the OH portion of this functional group. For example,

R—C (with =O and Cl) is an acid chloride;

R—C (with =O and NH_2) is an acid amide;

In this experiment we shall prepare two derivatives of acetic acid: an ester (ethyl acetate), and an amide (acetamide).

Ethyl acetate will be prepared by the reaction of ethanol (ethyl alcohol) and acetic acid:

$$C_2H_5OH + CH_3COOH = CH_3COOC_2H_5 + H_2O$$

The preparation of acetamide involves the heating of the ammonium salt of acetic acid:

$$CH_3COONH_4 = CH_3CONH_2 + H_2O$$

R—C (with =O and $O^-NH_4^+$) is the ammonium salt of the acid;

R—C (with =O and OR′) is an ester.

PROCEDURE

Caution: *Wear safety goggles throughout this experiment.*

Part I. Preparation of Ethyl Acetate, $CH_3COOC_2H_5$

a. Use a 25 × 200 mm test tube or a 50 ml erlenmeyer fitted with a one-hole stopper in which is inserted (barely through the stopper) a two-foot length of 8–10 mm glass tubing to serve as a condenser. The tubing must be open at both ends. See Appendix 2, Fig. 2-4.

b. Place 5 ml of ethanol, 6 ml of glacial acetic acid, and 8–10 drops of 18 M H_2SO_4 into the container.

c. Caution: Do not heat the reaction mixture directly with a flame since the organic liquids and their vapors are flammable. Clamp the container in an upright position partially immersed in a 250 ml beaker about half full of water. Attach the stopper and condenser tube. Heat the water until the reaction mixture is gently boiling. Continue heating for about 15 minutes. Allow to cool. Note the characteristic odor of the ester.

OPTIONAL. PURIFICATION OF THE ESTER

d. Attach the container to a condenser and heat with a boiling water bath until no more distillate comes over. (*Note:* If standard condensers are not available, a one-foot piece of 8–10 mm glass tubing with about a 100° bend near one end can serve as an air condenser. See Appendix 2, Figs. 2-1, 2-2, 2-3.) Collect the distillate in an 18 × 150 mm test tube. What remains behind in the reaction vessel?

e. Add to the distillate, a small amount at a time, about 2 ml of a saturated solution of sodium carbonate. If necessary, add more sodium carbonate solution until no further visible reaction is evident. Which of the two layers is the water layer?

f. Separate the two layers by decantation or use a separatory funnel if available. Discard the aqueous solution layer. Note the properties of the ester. Dry it with 0.5 g of anhydrous calcium chloride (or anhydrous magnesium sulfate) and distill it again if you wish to purify the sample further. Determine the weight of ester produced.

Part II. Preparation of Acetamide, CH₃CONH₂

a. Place 10 ml of glacial acetic acid in a 25 × 200 mm test tube or a 50 ml Erlenmeyer flask. Add 4 g of solid ammonium carbonate, $(NH_4)_2CO_3$, a little at a time to produce the ammonium salt of acetic acid.

b. After the evolution of $CO_2(g)$ has subsided somewhat (about 5 minutes) add two boiling chips. These minimize bumping while the solution is boiling. Clamp the test tube as in Part I*c*. Insert the stopper and air condenser used in Part I*a*. Heat with a small luminous flame for about 10 minutes.

c. Attach the test tube to an air condenser. (See note in Part I*d*.) Heat the test tube directly with a small flame and distill the mixture very slowly. Collect the distillate in successive small portions, about 1–2 ml each, in five or so small test tubes until the distillate begins to solidify. Change the receiving tube and collect the acetamide, which distills over (at about 215–225°C). You may have to warm the condenser carefully to keep it from becoming plugged with the solid product. If the distilling apparatus is quite hot, the acetamide may not solidify until it has been cooled in the test tube.

OPTIONAL. PURIFICATION OF THE AMIDE

d. If directed by your teacher, you may wish to purify the acetamide by recrystallization from acetone. **Caution:** Acetone is very flammable. Use an electric hot plate for evaporation of acetone. Do not use an open flame.

e. Determine the melting point of the purified acetamide. (See Fig. 26-2.) Determine the weight of acetamide produced.

QUESTIONS AND EXERCISES

1. (a) Calculate the number of moles of each reactant, C_2H_5OH and CH_3COOH, which were used in the preparation of $CH_3COOC_2H_5$.

   Data: 1 ml of C_2H_5OH weighs 0.79 g; 1 ml of CH_3COOH weighs 1.05 g.

   (b) Which reactant is present in excess?
   (c) If all of one of the reactants were consumed, how many moles of ethyl acetate could be produced? How many grams of $CH_3COOC_2H_5$ is this?

   (d) What is the role of the sulfuric acid in the reaction?

2. (a) Write the equation for the reaction of acetic acid with ammonium carbonate.
   (b) How many moles of each reactant CH_3COOH and $(NH_4)_2CO_3$, are involved in this reaction? If all of the $(NH_4)_2CO_3$ is converted to CH_3COONH_4 and then to CH_3CONH_2, how many moles and grams of acetamide would be expected?
   (c) How does the removal of water during the distillation in Part II*c* affect the yield of acetamide?

30

THE ELECTROLYSIS OF
AQUEOUS POTASSIUM IODIDE

You will recall that when water undergoes electrolysis the oxidation occurring at the anode produces oxygen gas while the reduction at the cathode produces hydrogen gas. Electrolysis of some aqueous salt solutions, however, may lead to oxidation or reduction of the ions from the salt if these ions are more readily oxidized or reduced than the water itself.

In this experiment you will electrolyze an aqueous solution of potassium iodide and then identify the products that are formed at the electrodes.

PROCEDURE

a. Set up the electrolysis apparatus as shown in Fig. 30-1. The U-tube is about 150 mm high and the electrodes are carbon rods. If the U-tube does not have side arms, be sure to use slotted corks to allow any gases formed to escape. The source of direct current should have a potential of about 12 volts.

b. Add enough 0.5 M potassium iodide solution to fill the U-tube to within 1 cm of the top. Make the electrical connections and allow the electrolysis to proceed for approximately 15 minutes.

c. Note and record any observable products and color changes which occur at the anode, where oxidation is occurring.

d. Note and record any observable changes at the cathode, where reduction is taking place.

e. Note the extent to which the brown color diffuses from the anode side of the U-tube into the cathode side.

f. Carefully remove the electrodes. Note the odor of the carbon anode.

g. Use a medicine dropper to draw off about 2 ml of the solution on the cathode side. Add a few drops of universal indicator (or phenolphthalein) to test the hydrogen ion concentration of the solution. Then add a few milliliters of 0.1 M ferric chloride solution and note the result.

h. Using a medicine dropper, draw off about

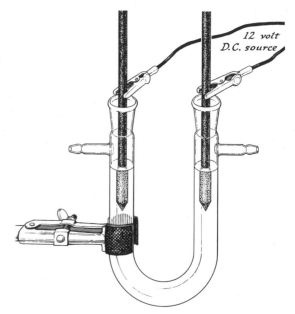

Fig. 30-1. **An electrolysis apparatus.**

2 ml of the dark brown liquid from the anode side. Add 1 ml of CCl_4, stopper, and shake the test tube for a few seconds. Allow the more dense carbon tetrachloride to settle and note the color of the two liquid layers.

Results

Record all observations neatly. Write equations for the electrode reactions you observed.

QUESTIONS

1. As iodine is produced at the anode it forms the brown complex ion I_3^- with the iodide ion of the electrolyte solution.

    (a) Write the equation for the reaction using reversible arrows to show the equilibrium involved.

    (b) What effect did the addition of CCl_4 have upon the equilibrium? Use your observations on the color of the two layers to explain the effect.

2. (a) What is the approximate hydrogen ion concentration around the cathode? What is the hydroxide ion concentration? Does the equation you wrote for the cathode half-reaction account for this result?

    (b) Write the equation for the reaction of 0.1 M $FeCl_3$ with the sample of solution taken from the cathode side.

3. When iodine, I_2, reacts with a basic solution, it undergoes a self-oxidation-reduction reaction to form iodide ions, I^-, and iodate ions, IO_3^-, both of which are colorless. Give a plausible explanation of the sharp color boundary noted near the bottom of the U-tube in terms of your knowledge of the products at each electrode. Write the equation for the reaction involved.

31

SOME CHEMISTRY OF IODINE

The following chart contains some of the known compounds of the halogens at various oxidation states. Note that the range in general extends from -1 to $+7$ but that fluorine differs significantly from the other halogens in that it has no stable oxyacids.

A glance at the chart should convince you that oxidation-reduction reactions are a very important part of halogen chemistry.

Although iodine will show some chemistry unique to itself, as every element will, many of its reactions are typical of other halogens. In Experiment 30 you prepared some iodine by electrolysis and observed some reactions of iodine which occurred within the U-tube. In this experiment we shall further investigate these and other reactions of iodine and note the influence of hydrogen ion concentration on the equilibria.

Oxidation State	Fluorine	Chlorine	Bromine	Iodine
$+7$		$HClO_4$, ClO_4^-		H_5IO_6, IO_4^-
$+5$		$HClO_3$, ClO_3^-	$HBrO_3$, BrO_3^-	HIO_3, IO_3^-
$+3$		$HClO_2$, ClO_2^-		
$+1$		$HClO$, ClO^-	$HBrO$, BrO^-	HIO, IO^-
0	F_2	Cl_2	Br_2	I_2
-1	HF, F^-	HCl, Cl^-	HBr, Br^-	HI, I^-

PROCEDURE

Caution: Solid iodine and its vapor will cause burns and stains on skin or clothing. Its vapors are poisonous and even small quantities will irritate the mucous membranes if inhaled. *Avoid unnecessary contact.*

Use 13×100 mm test tubes throughout this experiment except in Part II*b*.

Preliminary Experiment—The Starch Iodine Test

Prepare a dilute solution of iodine by adding one or two small iodine crystals to about 5 ml of tap water. Warm slightly, add 3 or 4 drops of starch solution, and observe. This is a very sensitive test for molecular iodine. Recall the iodine-clock reaction in Experiment 14.

Note: The color is due to a starch-iodine complex which is attributed to the ability of I_2 molecules to fit into the long, hollow spaces between the helical coils which constitute the starch molecule. The fit is close and the interaction strong enough to give the intense color even when very low concentrations of iodine are present.

Part I. Some Reactions of the Iodide Ion, I^-

a. To 2 ml of 0.1 M potassium iodide, KI, add an equal volume of 0.1 M silver nitrate, $AgNO_3$. Note the result.
b. To 2 ml of 0.1 M KI and 5 ml of starch solution add a drop or two of commercial bleach (5% NaOCl) solution. Note the result. Con-

tinue to add the bleaching solution until there is a second color change. How do you account for this?

c. To 2 ml of 0.1 M KI and 5 ml of starch solution add about 5 drops of 3% H_2O_2. Note the result.

Part II. Some Reactions of the Iodate Ion, IO_3^-

a. Pour about 5 ml of a saturated solution of KIO_3 into each of two test tubes.

(1) Add 3 ml of 0.1 M KI and 2 ml of 6 M H_2SO_4 to one of the test tubes. Decant the supernatant liquid from the solid produced. Filter, if necessary. Wash the solid with water. Do you recognize the solid? Run an identification test you have used previously to confirm your inference.

(2) Add 3 ml of 0.1 M KI and 2 ml of 6 M KOH to the second test tube. What do you conclude about the role of hydrogen ion in the reaction between iodide and iodate ions?

b. In a dry 18 × 150 mm test tube, place an amount of solid KIO_3 about the size of a pea and about twice as much sodium bisulfite, $Na_2S_2O_5$. Clamp the tube in an almost horizontal position and warm it gently with a small burner flame. Do not heat excessively. Note the product formed.

Part III. Reaction of I_2 in a Basic Solution

a. To a few crystals (about 0.5 g) of solid iodine add from a dropper about 10 drops of 6 M potassium hydroxide, KOH. Shake the test tube gently until the solid iodine disappears and the solution is colorless. You may need to warm the solution gently and add a few more drops of 6 M KOH. You will identify the product of this reaction in Part d.

b. Cool the solution and make it acid by adding sufficient (10 drops or slightly more) 6 M HNO_3 to neutralize the base added previously. Note the product of this reaction. What do you think it is?

c. Make the solution basic again by adding a few drops of 6 M KOH. Warm gently and add a few drops of 6 M KOH if necessary until a color change is observed. Discard the solution.

d. Repeat the procedure outlined in Part a. Cool under the cold water tap until a solid crystallizes from the solution. Decant the supernatant liquid and save it for part (2) below.

(1) Dry the white solid by heating the test tube gently. Allow it to cool. To the cool white solid add a small amount (about 0.2 g) of solid sodium bisulfite, $Na_2S_2O_5$. Mix the solids by stirring gently with a stirring rod. Heat the mixture with a small flame. Note the result. Compare it with that obtained in Part IIb. *Do not inhale the vapors.*

(2) To the decanted liquid add 5–10 drops of 0.1 M silver nitrate, $AgNO_3$; shake the test tube and note the result. Compare the product with that obtained in Part Ia.

QUESTIONS

1. Write the equations for the reactions observed in Parts Ia, Ib, Ic.

2. (a) How did the results in Part IIId(1) compare with those obtained in Part IIb?
   (b) How did the test with 0.1 M silver nitrate in Part IIId(2) compare with the results of Part Ia?
   (c) What do you conclude about the ionic species formed when I_2 reacts with 6 M KOH as in Part IIIa?

3. Write the equation for the self-oxidation-reduction reaction of iodine in a basic solution. Write the equation for the reverse of this reaction in an acid solution.

4. In which oxidation state do the halogens most commonly occur in nature? Explain your answer in terms of the electronic structure of this species for chlorine.

5. How would you prepare elemental fluorine, F_2? Consult the oxidation-reduction table in Appendix 8 to check the feasibility of your method.

6. Sodium iodate can be obtained from the plateaus of Chile. Suggest a commercial method for obtaining elemental iodine from this source.

32

SOME CHEMISTRY OF THE THIRD-ROW ELEMENTS

H																	He
Li	Be											B	C	N	O	F	Ne
Na	Mg											Al	Si	P	S	Cl	Ar
K	Ca	Sc	Ti	V	Cr	Mn	Fe	Co	Ni	Cu	Zn	Ga	Ge	As	Se	Br	Kr

In this experiment we shall observe some of the properties of the elements in the third row of the periodic table and attempt to answer the following questions: Is there an observable trend in the physical appearance, the electrical conductivity, and the reactivity with water going across Row 3? How do the basic or acidic properties of the hydroxides vary from left to right?

Your teacher will demonstrate some of the properties of the third-row elements. As these tests are performed, answer the following questions from your observations:

(1) Describe the appearance of each of the third-row elements as they are exhibited. Which appear to have reacted with air?
(2) What trend in reactivity with water is indicated?
  (a) Are the resulting solutions acidic or basic?
  (b) Rank the elements in order of their ability to reduce water to produce hydrogen gas.
(3) What is the trend in electrical conductivity of these elements?

STUDENT EXPERIMENT

COMPARISON OF THE RELATIVE ACID-BASE STRENGTH OF THE HYDROXIDES OF ROW 3

PROCEDURE

Prepare approximately 0.5 M aqueous solutions of the soluble oxides or hydroxides of these third-row elements: Na, P, S, Cl. Use slurries (suspensions) of the slightly soluble oxides or hydroxides of Mg, Al, Si. Use 18 × 150 mm test tubes and retain all solutions for subsequent tests described in Steps a and b.

$NaOH$. Add 0.2 g of sodium oxide, Na_2O, or 0.1g of sodium peroxide, Na_2O_2, to 10 ml of water.
$Mg(OH)_2$. Add 0.2 g of magnesium oxide, MgO, to 10 ml of water.
$Al(OH)_3$. Use the freshly prepared slurry of $Al(OH)_3(s)$ furnished by your teacher *or* prepare some $Al(OH)_3(s)$ by adding dropwise

about 3 ml of 6 M $NH_3(aq)$ to 7 ml of 1 M aluminum nitrate solution. Boil gently for a minute. Allow the precipitate to settle, then decant and discard the supernatant liquid. Wash the precipitate with distilled water. Decant and discard the wash water. Add about 10 ml of distilled water and shake the mixture to form a slurry.

SiO$_2$ · nH$_2$O. Add 0.3 g of hydrous silicon dioxide, $SiO_2 · nH_2O$, to 10 ml of water.

PO(OH)$_3$. **Caution:** *Vigorous reaction!* Add 0.07 g of phosphorus pentoxide, P_4O_{10}, a little at a time to about 10 ml of water.

SO$_2$(OH)$_2$. Use 10 ml of 0.5 M sulfuric acid solution.

ClO$_3$(OH). Use 10 ml of 0.5 M perchloric acid solution.

a. Determine the approximate hydrogen ion concentration of each of the aqueous solutions or slurries of the hydroxides with appropriate indicators. Indicators with a wide range, such as Hydrion paper or a few drops of universal indicator solution, are convenient.

b. Divide each of the slurries of the slightly soluble hydroxides into two parts. Test one portion of each with 1–2 ml of 6 M HCl added a few drops at a time. Shake the test tube occasionally as the acid is added. The Hydrion paper or the universal indicator added above indicate the degree of acidity. Note any changes. Test the remaining portion of the slurry with 1–2 ml of 6 M NaOH added a few drops at a time until the solution is definitely basic. Shake the test tube occasionally and note any changes.

QUESTIONS AND EXERCISES

1. Write an equation for each reaction between a third-row element and water as observed in the class experiment.

2. Write an equation for each reaction observed between each of the oxides Na_2O, MgO, P_4O_{10}, and water.

3. Write an equation for each reaction observed between a slightly soluble hydroxide of a third-row element and the following: (a) 6 M HCl; (b) 6 M NaOH.

4. (a) Which of the seven hydroxide solutions were acidic? Which of the seven hydroxide solutions were basic?

(b) How does their basicity and acidity correlate with their position in the third row?

5. Which of the slightly soluble hydroxides is amphoteric—that is, which dissolved in both 6 M HCl and 6 M NaOH and thus showed both basic and acidic properties.

6. What can be deduced concerning the strength of the H—O bonds in the hydroxides that have acidic properties compared with those that have basic properties?

7. Draw diagrams to show the spatial arrangement of the atoms in the hydroxides of sulfur, phosphorus, and chlorine. (H_2SO_4, H_3PO_4, $HClO_4$.)

33

EXPERIMENTS 33-36 CONSTITUTE A BRIEF INTRODUCTION TO QUALITATIVE ANALYSIS

DEVELOPMENT OF A SCHEME OF QUALITATIVE ANALYSIS USING REAGENTS LABELED *A, B, C*

In this experiment you are to discover what differentiating properties four solutions, labeled I, II, III, and IV, exhibit when each reacts with three reagents labeled *A, B, C*. You should observe which reactions involve the formation of precipitates, note color changes and other evidences of reaction. After you have recorded the results in tabular form, study the table carefully and develop a method for discriminating between the four solutions.

Consider the following hypothetical case, in which reagents labeled *X, Y,* and *Z* were allowed to react with samples of each of the unknown solutions I, II, III, and IV.

	Reagents		
Solutions	*X*	*Y*	*Z*
I	−	+ (yellow)	+ (yellow)
II	+ (white)	−	+ (white)
III	−	−	+ (blue)
IV	−	+ (white)	−

The + means a distinctive reaction was observed and the − means no evidence of reaction was noted. The color of precipitates or changes in color of solutions are also noted. If you were given an unknown, which you were told was either solution I, II, III, or IV, what method would you outline to identify the unknown by its reactions with reagents *X, Y,* and *Z*? How many tests are involved? If an unknown gives a − test with *X* and a + test with *Y*, will this identify it? Suppose another unknown gives a + test with *X*; is this sufficient to identify it?

This reasoning is used in a branch of chemistry, *qualitative analysis*, to develop schemes to separate and identify substances present in mixtures. In Experiments 34, 35, and 36 you will apply this method to the development of a method to analyze solutions containing certain cations or anions using labeled reagents. In this experiment the solutions and reagents are deliberately *not* labeled so that you can focus your attention on the reasoning that must be applied to develop an analytical scheme from tabulated results of the differentiating properties.

PROCEDURE

a. Use clean 13 × 100 mm test tubes, rinsed with distilled water. Use about 1 ml of each solution or reagent for each test. Agitate the tube gently to make sure the reactants are mixed.

b. Organize a table comparable to that developed in the introduction of this experiment.

c. Make the tests on each of the solutions I, II, III, and IV with reagents A, B, and C. Record your results as + or − but also note any distinctive characteristics of each precipitate and any changes in color which occur.

d. Study the data table carefully and note the differentiating reactions. Obtain an unknown solution from your teacher and test it to determine whether it is solution I, II, III, or IV. Report your analysis together with a summary of the evidence which supports it.

e. Secure another unknown which contains a mixture of *two* or *more* of the solutions. Study the data table carefully for information which will enable you to determine when a given combination of the solutions is present. You may assume that the solutions I, II, III, and IV do not react with each other. Make the tests and report the result to your teacher. Summarize the supporting evidence.

34

THE RELATIVE SOLUBILITIES OF SOME COMPOUNDS OF THE METALS OF THE SECOND COLUMN—QUALITATIVE ANALYSIS

The elements of the second column of the periodic table have only two common oxidation states, 0 and +2. The chemistry of these elements is so similar that they are difficult to separate. Many of their compounds are slightly soluble but it is possible, by choosing the proper anion, to find differences in solubility which will permit you to separate the cations of these metals.

In this experiment you will study the effect of adding reagents containing selected anions to solutions containing the cations of the metals of the second column. After a systematic study of the relative solubilities of their carbonates, chromates, sulfates, oxalates, and hydroxides you should be able to make a qualitative analysis of an unknown solution containing one or more of these cations.

PROCEDURE

Organize a table in which you can record your results obtained when each solution containing a cation of the second column is tested with each of the reagents listed below.

The solutions are:

0.1 M $Ba(NO_3)_2$, a source for Ba^{+2}
0.1 M $Sr(NO_3)_2$ for Sr^{+2}
0.1 M $Ca(NO_3)_2$ for Ca^{+2}
0.1 M $Mg(NO_3)_2$ for Mg^{+2}

The reagents are:

2 M $(NH_4)_2CO_3$ [containing some $NH_3(aq)$] a source for CO_3^{-2}
0.5 M K_2CrO_4 for CrO_4^{-2}
0.2 M $(NH_4)_2C_2O_4$ for $C_2O_4^{-2}$
1 M $(NH_4)_2SO_4$ for SO_4^{-2}
6 M $NH_3(aq)$ for OH^-

a. Use clean 13 × 100 mm test tubes. Test 1 ml (about 20 drops) of each of the solutions of the metal nitrates with 1 ml of each of the reagents.

b. In cases where precipitates of the carbonates are formed, heat the test tube in a boiling water bath to aid in precipitation. Cool the test tube and allow the precipitate to settle. Use a centrifuge if available. Decant the supernatant liquid and discard it. Add enough 6 M HCl, a drop at a time, to the precipitate until it dissolves. Use these samples for flame tests.

c. Flame test—an additional confirmatory test: Obtain a flame testing wire (platinum or nichrome). from your teacher. Clean the wire by heating it to incandescence in the hottest part of the flame of the burner and then dip the heated wire into about 5 ml of 12 M HCl in a test tube. Heat the wire again after dipping in the concentrated HCl (chlorides of the metals are readily volatilized). Traces of sodium cause a flash of yellow which may be difficult to eliminate.

Dip the clean wire into the test solution prepared in Step b. and then heat the wire in the burner flame. Note the characteristic flame color for each of the solutions tested. Clean the wire as directed above before dipping it in a different solution. Use the flame test on a solution containing a mixture of the cations. In what order do the flame colors appear?

d. Study the data table carefully, then obtain an unknown solution containing *one* of the cations of the second column and test it to determine if it contains Mg^{+2}, Ca^{+2}, Sr^{+2} or Ba^{+2}. Report your analysis together with a summary of the evidence which supports it.

e. *Optional*. Secure another unknown which contains a mixture of two or more of the cations of the second column. Study the data table carefully and answer the questions below. Outline a series of sequential tests and report the result to your teacher. Include the supporting evidence.

QUESTIONS

1. (a) Which carbonate of the second column metals has the greatest solubility? Which ones have a similar solubility?
   (b) Describe a possible separation of the cations based upon the above differences.

2. (a) Which chromate of these metals is the least soluble?
   (b) How can this difference in solubility be used in an analytical separation of a solution containing 0.1 *M* solutions of Sr^{+2} and Ba^{+2}?

3. With which of the anions does the Mg^{+2} ion have the lowest solubility of all the cations?

4. Which oxalate of these metals is the most soluble?

5. The solubility product constants, K_{sp}, for the sulfates of the cations of the second column are ($MgSO_4$ is very soluble):

$$CaSO_4 \quad 2.4 \times 10^{-5}$$
$$SrSO_4 \quad 7.6 \times 10^{-7}$$
$$BaSO_4 \quad 1.5 \times 10^{-9}$$

If a 0.002 *M* solution of $(NH_4)_2SO_4$ were added to an equal volume of 0.002 *M* solutions of each of the cations of the second column, in which case would a precipitate form?

35

QUALITATIVE ANALYSIS OF Ag^+, Hg_2^{+2}, AND Pb^{+2}

Only three of the common metal ions, Ag^+, Hg_2^{+2}, and Pb^{+2}, form slightly soluble chlorides. Because of this, it is possible to separate these ions from other cations as slightly soluble chlorides and then identify each on the basis of distinguishing reactions of their chlorides.

In the first part of this experiment you will become familiar with a few reactions used to identify the silver, mercurous and lead ions in solution. From these observations you will be able to devise a method by which you can analyze an unknown solution and determine the presence or absence of each ion.

PROCEDURE

a. Use clean 13×100 mm test tubes for all the tests. Prepare a sample of each of AgCl, Hg_2Cl_2, and $PbCl_2$ by adding 10 drops of 6 M HCl to 1 ml of each of the 0.1 M test solutions [$AgNO_3$, $Hg_2(NO_3)_2$, and $Pb(NO_3)_2$]. You may need to cool the test tube containing the Pb^{+2} ions to obtain a precipitate. Prepare a table for all observations.

b. Start heating a 100 ml beaker half full of water to serve as a hot water bath. Allow the chloride precipitates to settle in each tube. Use a centrifuge if available. Decant and discard the supernatant liquid. Add about 2 ml of water to each precipitate and, with frequent agitation, heat to boiling temperature in the boiling water bath for a minute or two. Which of the chlorides is soluble in hot water?

c. From the test tube showing the greatest solubility in hot water remove about 5 drops of the hot solution with a medicine dropper and transfer it to a clean test tube. Add 5 drops of 0.1 M potassium chromate, K_2CrO_4, solution and note the result.

d. Remove the three test tubes from the hot water bath and cool them under cold water from the tap. Shake the test tubes occasionally. Allow each precipitate to settle and decant the supernatant liquid from each. Discard the liquid but retain any precipitates remaining for additional tests.

e. Add 2 or 3 ml of 6 M $NH_3(aq)$ to each of the remaining precipitates. Shake the test tubes and note the results. To the test tube(s) in which the precipitate dissolved, add about 3 ml of 6 M HNO_3 and note the result.

f. Examine your results and use them to develop a scheme by which you could identify the presence of one, two, or all three of these cations in an unknown solution. Organize your scheme in such a way that another student could follow it.

g. Obtain an unknown from your teacher and analyze it for the presence of one or more of the cations tested in this experiment. Report your results together with supporting evidence as directed by your teacher.

QUESTIONS AND EXERCISES

1. Write equations for all reactions occurring in this experiment.
2. Construct an outline (flow diagram) which summarizes the steps you would use to analyze an unknown containing all three cations, Ag^+, Hg_2^{+2}, and Pb^{+2}.

36

DEVELOPMENT OF A SCHEME FOR THE ANALYSIS OF AN UNKNOWN CONTAINING VARIOUS ANIONS

In Experiment 33 you considered the principles involved in developing a scheme of qualitative analysis with a group of unlabeled solutions. In this experiment you will observe and record some characteristic chemical reactions of several negatively charged ions: SO_4^{-2}, CO_3^{-2}, Cl^-, and I^-, using selected reagents. From a study of these observations you will be able to develop a method for identifying each of these ions in the presence of the other ions.

Your work will be typical of the work done by chemists who develop more elaborate schemes which can be used to identify dozens of cations and anions in a given sample.

PROCEDURE

a. Organize a table in which you can record your observations for the results obtained by adding each of the reagents to the solutions of each anion to be studied.

   The *solutions* containing anions to be studied are:

   0.1 M sodium sulfate, Na_2SO_4, for SO_4^{-2} ions;

   0.5 M sodium carbonate, Na_2CO_3, for CO_3^{-2} ions;

   0.1 M sodium chloride, NaCl, for Cl^- ions;

   0.1 M sodium iodide, NaI, for I^- ions.

   The *reagents* with which these are to be tested are:

   0.1 M barium nitrate, $Ba(NO_3)_2$, for Ba^{+2} ions;

   0.1 M silver nitrate, $AgNO_3$, for Ag^+ ions;
   1.0 M nitric acid, HNO_3, for H^+ ions.

   Use clean 13 × 100 mm test tubes for all tests.

b. Test 5–10 drops of each solution separately with 3–5 drops of the 0.1 M $Ba(NO_3)_2$ reagent. Record the results observed. To each test tube that contains a precipitate add 5–10 drops of 1.0 M HNO_3 and record any changes you observe.

c. Test 5–10 drops of each solution separately with 3–5 drops of the 0.1 M $AgNO_3$ reagent. Record the results observed. To each test tube that contains a precipitate add 5–10 drops of 1.0 M HNO_3 and record any changes you observe.

d. Prepare new samples of the silver precipitates which formed in Step *c*. Add 5–10 drops of 6 M aqueous ammonia, $NH_3(aq)$ to the precipitates and record any changes you observe.

e. Test 5–10 drops of each solution separately with 3–5 drops of 1.0 M HNO_3 and record the results.

f. Examine the pattern of reactions shown by your table of observations. Develop a scheme by which you could identify one or a combination of two of the anions in a single solution. Organize your scheme in such a way that another student could follow it. You may wish to try it out by making up your own "trial unknowns" containing various combinations of the anions.

g. Obtain an unknown from your teacher and analyze it for the four anions. Report your results. Include supporting evidence for your conclusions.

EXERCISES

1. Write net ionic equations for the precipitation reactions which occurred when solutions of the anions were mixed with the solution containing Ba^{+2} ions.

2. Do the same for the precipitation reactions which occurred in Part c with the Ag^+ ions.

3. Write equations for the reactions which occurred when the precipitates were acidified with 1.0 M HNO_3.

4. Write equations for the reactions which occurred when the silver precipitates reacted with aqueous ammonia to form the complex ion, $Ag(NH_3)_2{}^+$.

37

THE SEPARATION OF SOME TRANSITION METAL IONS WITH AN ANION EXCHANGE RESIN

Ion exchange resins are high molecular weight polymers or resins which contain a framework of covalently bonded carbon and hydrogen atoms. The resins have centers of high positive or negative charge attached to the framework. A typical structure for a portion of a resin polymer is

About one ring in ten is cross-linked into two other chains of the polymer to give it a three-dimensional structure. The groups designated by an —X determine the resin type. If they are —COOH or —SO_3H groups, cations will be exchanged for the hydrogens. This is the type that is used in water softeners in which objectionable ions such as Ca^{+2} and Mg^{+2} are exchanged for H^+.

If the —X groups are substituted ammonium groups such as —$N(CH_3)_3^+Cl^-$, anions will be exchanged for the chloride ions. In this experiment you will use an anion-exchange resin of this type because some of the metal ions used will be converted to complex chloride ions such as $FeCl_6^{-3}$ and $CoCl_4^-$. For example, when a salt

containing the hydrated ferric ion is dissolved in 9 M HCl, a complex ion is formed:

$$Fe(H_2O)_6^{+3} + 6\,Cl^- \rightleftharpoons FeCl_6^{-3} + 6\,H_2O$$

The complex anions will be exchanged for the chloride ions of the resin. If the concentration of the chloride ion is then decreased by using 5 M HCl and finally 1 M HCl, the chloride complexes will successively shift their equilibria to form the hydrated metal cations which are no longer retained by the resin and can be washed through (eluted from) the column. The chloride complex which forms the least stable complex will be eluted even at the higher concentration of the chloride ion (9 M HCl), while the most stable complex will not be eluted until the chloride ion concentration has been reduced to that of 1 M HCl.

The ions of three closely related transition metals—iron, cobalt and nickel—were selected because each has a characteristic color in solutions containing chloride ions and can thus be readily distinguished as they are washed off the resin. The test solution you will use will contain salts of iron, cobalt, and nickel dissolved in 12 M HCl.

After the ions have been separated on the anion exchange column you will test the eluted samples to determine the efficiency of the separations.

PROCEDURE

a. Obtain an ion exchange column and set it up as shown in Fig. 37-1. Attach a piece of white paper with plastic tape so you can distinguish the characteristic colors of the anions as they come off the column. The solution on

the column is 2 M HCl. Leave this on the column until you are ready to add another solution. *Do not allow the column to run dry* since this may lead to uneven flow (channeling) later and decrease the efficiency of the

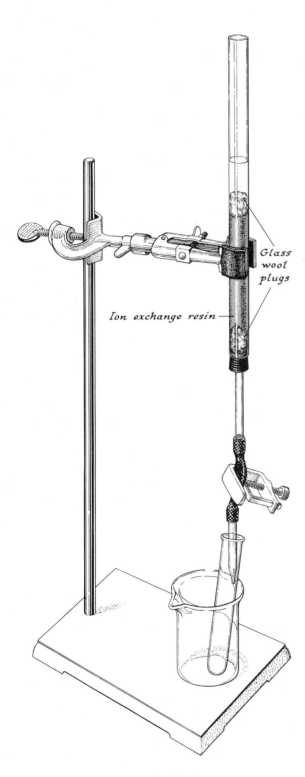

Glass wool plugs

Ion exchange resin

separation. *Either add the next solution or close the screw clamp whenever the level of the liquid in the tube drops to the glasswool plug at the top of the column.*

b. Obtain about 50 ml of 9 *M* HCl solution. From this prepare 45 ml of 1 *M* HCl solution by diluting 5 ml 9 *M* HCl with 40 ml of distilled water. Prepare 30 ml of 5 *M* HCl by mixing 15 ml 9 *M* HCl with 15 ml 1 *M* HCl. Place each of these solutions in clean labeled beakers for use when needed. Obtain about 2 ml of the test solution containing the three ions to be separated.

c. Open the screw clamp to allow the 2 *M* HCl solution already on the column to drop to the level of the top glasswool plug. Add 9 *M* HCl to refill to the top of the tube. Adjust the screw clamp so the flow will be about 2.5 ml per minute.

d. When the 9 *M* HCl has dropped to the top of the glasswool plug, close the clamp and *add the 2 ml of the colored test solution.* Open the clamp to obtain the same rate of flow as before.

e. When the level again drops to the glasswool plug, add 5 ml of 9 *M* HCl. Collect 5 ml of eluate (the solution that passes through the column). Add another 5 ml portion of 9 *M* HCl and collect 5 ml of eluate in a separate test tube. Repeat this procedure with another 5 ml of 9 *M* HCl. Label the three test tubes e-1, e-2, and e-3. Note the color of the eluate in each test tube.

f. Repeat Step *e*, except use four 5 ml portions of 5 *M* HCl solution in place of the 9 *M* HCl. Collect the eluate, about 5 ml in each of four test tubes labeled f-1, f-2, f-3, and f-4.

g. Repeat Step *e*, using four or five 5 ml portions of 1 *M* HCl solution. Collect the eluate, about 5 ml in each test tube labeled g-1, g-2, etc.

h. After the last 5 ml portion of 1 *M* HCl solution drops to the glasswool plug at the top of the column, add 10 ml of distilled water to rinse the resin. Dilute 4 ml of 9 *M* HCl with 14 ml of water to make some 2 *M* HCl solution. Add this to the column so it will be ready for use again by another student. Close the clamp when the acid level is about 2 cm above the top of the glasswool plug.

i. Identify the different colored solutions by comparing them with hydrochloric acid solutions of iron, cobalt, and nickel chlorides which your teacher will have available.

Fig. 37-1. **An ion-exchange column.**

j. Test a drop of each eluted sample separately with each of the reagents to determine the efficiency of the separation. Place the drops on a glass plate on a piece of white paper.

(1) Add a drop of 0.1 M KSCN solution. A blood-red coloration due to formation of $Fe(SCN)^{+2}$ ion indicates the presence of Fe^{+3} ion.

(2) Place a fresh drop of each eluate on the glass plate. Make each basic by adding a few drops of 15 M NH_3 solution. **Caution:** The solution will get hot during neutraliza-tion. Use litmus to check when basic, then add a drop of dimethyl glyoxime reagent. A brilliant red precipitate indicates the presence of nickel.

(3) Place a fresh drop of each eluate on the glass plate. Add a drop of 10% solution of NH_4SCN in acetone to each drop being tested. The appearance of a blue color due to the formation of $Co(SCN)_4^{-2}$ ions indicates the presence of Co^{+2} ions.

Record all observations neatly, in tabular form when appropriate.

QUESTIONS

1. One of the metallic ions was eluted with 9 M HCl. It would also have been eluted with the 5 M or 1 M HCl solutions. Which one was it? Give a reason for this ease of elution in terms of the stability of its complex chloride anions.

2. The color of some of the ions on the column was different from the color of the final eluate. Explain this in terms of the composition of the complex ions.

3. What are the conditions which favor the release of ions from the column?

4. Recalling that the resin used is an anion exchange type, which of the metallic ions in this experiment forms the most stable complex chloride anion?

38

SOME INVESTIGATIONS INTO THE CORROSION OF IRON

Each year the United States alone loses an estimated six billion dollars as a result of the corrosion of steel. What are some of the factors which are responsible for this loss? What can be done to reduce this loss?

Corrosion is a general term applied to the process in which uncombined metals are converted to oxides or other compounds. This causes the gradual deterioration of metals. Although the detailed chemistry of the corrosion of iron is not completely understood, it clearly involves oxidation by some oxidizing agent. In this experiment we shall investigate some of the factors involved in corrosion and try to relate them by some generalizations.

PROCEDURE

Part I. Reactions of Iron with Various Aqueous Reagents

a. Place a clean, bright nail in each of five test tubes. Slide each nail carefully down the side to avoid breaking the bottom of the test tube.
b. Partially fill each of the test tubes with one of the following reagents so that the nail is just covered. Your teacher will tell you which one of the groups to use. All solutions are 0.1 M.

Group A	Group B	Group C
NaOH	KOH	Na_3PO_4
$Na_2Cr_2O_7$	Na_2CO_3	$Na_2C_2O_4$
NaCl	KNO_3	NaSCN
HCl	HNO_3	H_2SO_4
Distilled water	Distilled water	Distilled water

c. Determine the approximate hydrogen ion concentration of each solution using litmus paper, Hydrion paper, or other indicator solutions. It is sufficient to record simply whether the solution is acidic, basic or neutral. Go on to Part II.
d. Allow the nails to stand overnight in the solutions. Observe and record any changes that have taken place. Compare your results with those of students using the other sets of reagents. Record their results along with yours in tabular form.
e. After the solutions have stood overnight, add one or two drops of 0.1 M potassium ferricyanide, $K_3Fe(CN)_6$, which contains the ions K^+ and $Fe(CN)_6^{-3}$, to each solution and observe any change.
f. Add one drop of 0.1 M potassium ferricyanide solution to about 1 ml of ferrous sulfate solution. Compare this result to that obtained when the potassium ferricyanide was added to the various solutions containing nails. What conclusions can be made from the results in Step e?

Part II. Reactions Involving Metal Couples—Two Metals in Contact

a. Prepare about 200 ml of agar-agar solution as follows: Heat about 200 ml of distilled water to a gentle boil. Remove the burner and stir in 2 g of powdered agar-agar. Continue the heating and stir until the agar is dispersed.
b. Add about 10 drops of 0.1 M potassium ferri-

cyanide and 5 drops of 0.1% phenolphthalein indicator to the agar-agar solution. Stir thoroughly.

c. While the agar-agar solution is cooling, prepare four clean bright nails as shown in Fig. 38-1. Place one nail on one side of a petri dish or small beaker. Bend another nail sharply with a pair of pliers and place it on the other side of the dish. Twist a clean piece of bare copper wire around a third nail. Then remove the nail and tighten the wire coil so that when the nail is forced back through it makes tight contact with the wire. Place this in a second dish.

Repeat the above procedure using a zinc strip on a fourth nail. If a strip of zinc is not available, a piece of mossy zinc may be attached by forcing the nail through the zinc piece in at least two places. Place this nail in the second petri dish as shown in Fig. 38-1. Be sure the nails do not touch one another.

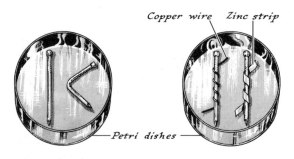

Fig. 38-1. **Studying the corrosion of iron.**

d. When the agar-agar solution has cooled to lukewarm, and is still fluid, pour it carefully into the petri dishes until the nails and metals are covered to a depth of about 0.5 cm.

e. Make observations during the time remaining in the class period. Place the dishes in your locker and observe them again after they have stood overnight.

QUESTIONS AND EXERCISES

1. List the reagents in Part I where no indication of corrosion was observed.

2. List the reagents in Part I in which there was an indication of corrosion.

3. Are any regularities in evidence? What is the evidence? How do you account for the regularity?

4. What did you observe regarding the reactions at the head, the pointed end or at the sharp bend of the nail which were different from the rest of the nail? Account for this in terms of the mechanical treatment of the nail during its manufacture.

5. Why is it that a nail can stand for many days on the shelf in a hardware store and not rust, but when placed in tap water it quickly rusts?

6. Ferrous ions react with potassium ferricyanide to form a colored precipitate. Write the equation for the reaction.

7. Which color in Part II indicates the site of the oxidation reaction? Which the site of the reduction? Account for the formation of each color.

8. Write the oxidation and reduction reactions for each case in which you observed a reaction in Part II.

9. Consult the $E°$ table in Appendix 8 and predict another metal that is more readily oxidized than iron and will protect it from corrosion. Test your prediction by an experiment.

10. How does a coating of zinc on iron (galvanized iron), protect iron from corrosion?

11. Magnesium metal rods are sometimes placed in hot water heaters. Why?

39

PREPARATION OF A COMPLEX SALT AND A DOUBLE SALT

Many salts crystallize out of aqueous solution as hydrates—for example, $CuSO_4 \cdot 5H_2O$, $FeSO_4 \cdot 7H_2O$, or $Al_2(SO_4)_3 \cdot 9H_2O$. The building blocks in the crystals are hydrated cations and anions such as $Cu(H_2O)_4^{+2}$, and $SO_4(H_2O)^{-2}$ in the case of $CuSO_4 \cdot 5H_2O$.

Many of the transition metals form stable complex ions in which the metal ion is bound to molecules (or ions) other than water—for example, $Co(NH_3)_6^{+3}$ or $Fe(CN)_6^{-3}$. Salts containing such complex ions as these are called coordination compounds or complex salts—for example, hexaamminecobalt(III) chloride, $Co(NH_3)_6Cl_3$, and potassium hexacyanoferrate(III), $K_3Fe(CN)_6$. The building blocks in the crystalline solids are shown in Fig. 39-1.

Double salts are formed when two salts crystallize out together in simple molecular proportions. They have their own crystal form, which need not be the same as that of either of the component salts. The alums are double salts with the general formula $M^+M^{+3}(SO_4^{-2})_2 \cdot 12H_2O$, of which potassium alum, $KAl(SO_4)_2 \cdot 12H_2O$, is a common example. Another class has the formula $M^{+2}M_2^+(SO_4^{-2})_2 \cdot 6H_2O$, of which ferrous ammonium sulfate, $Fe(NH_4)_2(SO_4)_2 \cdot 6H_2O$, is an example. Double salts in solution exhibit the properties of each of the ions (usually hydrated) present in their component salts.

Examples of double salts and complex salts are extremely abundant. In this experiment you will prepare a sample of each type.

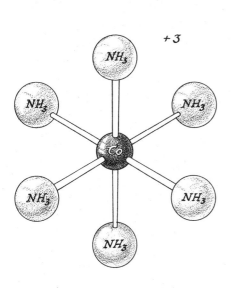

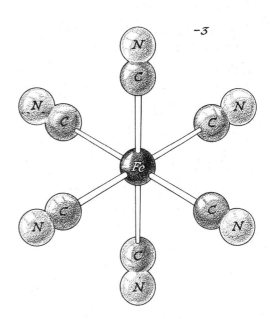

Fig. 39-1. **The structure of some complex ions.**

PROCEDURE

Part I. Preparation of A Double Salt: Cupric Ammonium Sulfate, $CuSO_4 \cdot (NH_4)_2SO_4 \cdot 6H_2O$

a. Dissolve 0.02 mole of cupric sulfate pentahydrate, $CuSO_4 \cdot 5H_2O$ (249.5 g/mole), and 0.02 mole of ammonium sulfate, $(NH_4)_2SO_4$ (132 g/mole), in 10 ml of water. Heat gently until the salts are dissolved.

b. Allow the solution to cool slowly to room temperature until crystals form. Larger crystals may be obtained by allowing the solution to stand overnight. While crystallization is proceeding, go on to Part II.

c. Cool the mixture further in a cold water bath, then decant the solution off the crystals.

d. Dry the crystals on a filter paper using a paper towel as a blotter. Examine them carefully and describe them in your lab notebook. These crystals belong to the monoclinic system.

e. Weigh the dry crystals. Note the number of moles of reactants used and moles of products formed. Calculate the percentage yield you obtained.

Part II. A Complex Salt: Tetraamminecopper(II) Sulfate Monohydrate, $Cu(NH_3)_4SO_4 \cdot H_2O$

a. Place 8 ml of 15 M ammonia water diluted with 5 ml of distilled water in a small evaporating dish.

b. Weigh 0.02 mole of $CuSO_4 \cdot 5H_2O$ (249.5 g/mole). Use a mortar and pestle to pulverize the cupric sulfate crystals, if necessary. Add the powdered crystals to the ammonia solution and stir until all of the cupric sulfate pentahydrate is dissolved.

c. Pour 8 ml of ethyl alcohol slowly down the side of the dish so as to cover the solution with alcohol. Do not stir or agitate the mixture. Cover with a watch glass and let it stand overnight.

d. After the mixture has been allowed to stand

overnight, stir slowly and gently to insure complete precipitation. Allow the crystals to settle. Decant and discard the supernatant liquid. Transfer the crystals to a filter by rinsing with 3–5 ml portions of a mixture of equal volumes of 15 M $NH_3(aq)$ and ethyl alcohol.

e. Finally, wash the crystals on the funnel with 5 ml of ethyl alcohol. Attach the hose from an aspirator to the funnel stem to draw the liquid from the crystals. Apply the suction gently to avoid tearing the filter paper. Repeat the washing and drying operation.

f. Remove the filter paper and spread it out on a paper towel.

g. Weigh the dry crystals. Did you obtain 0.02 mole of the complex salt? How many moles of NH_3 were used?

Part III. Comparison of Some of the Properties of a Single Salt, a Double Salt, and a Complex Salt

a. Place a small amount (about 1 ml) of *anhydrous* cupric sulfate crystals into a small, dry test tube. Note the change in color which takes place when 2 or 3 ml of water are added. Now add 6 M ammonia solution a few drops at a time until 5 ml have been added. Record your observations.

b. Dissolve a small amount of the double salt you prepared in Part I in about 5 ml of water in a large test tube. Make a similar solution using the complex salt from Part II. Compare the colors of the solutions. What ionic species present in each solution are responsible for the color? Dilute each solution with about 20 ml of water and record any changes in color.

c. Place small quantities of each of the dry salts you prepared in separate small test tubes. Heat each gently and note any color changes. Identify the gas given off from each sample.

QUESTIONS

1. In Part III*a*, account for the successive color changes noted in terms of the structure of the ion containing copper.

2. What are the ionic species present when the double

salt cupric ammonium sulfate dissolves in water?

3. What are the ionic species present when the complex salt tetrammine copper(II) sulfate dissolves in a small quantity of water? Give a reasonable ex-

planation of the changes which took place as more water was added.

4. Account for the changes you noted when each salt was heated.

5. From the evidence obtained in this experiment, list the ionic species which constitute the fundamental building blocks in crystals of:

(a) cupric sulfate (anhydrous),

(b) cupric sulfate pentahydrate,

(c) cupric ammonium sulfate hexahydrate,

(d) tetraamminecopper(II) sulfate monohydrate.

6. Why was a yield of 0.02 mole expected for each of the salts you prepared?

40

PREPARATION OF POTASSIUM DICHROMATE

The transition metals can form compounds containing the elements in a variety of oxidation states. In the next two experiments you will study some of the oxidation-reduction chemistry of chromium as you prepare some common compounds of this element. In the chart below note the color and formulas for the ionic species of chromium with various oxidation numbers which are present in the acidic and basic solutions. Use this chart to follow the reactions as you prepare potassium dichromate, $K_2Cr_2O_7$, from chromium(III) acetate, $Cr(CH_3COO)_3 \cdot H_2O$.

Oxidation Number of Chromium	Ionic Species Present	
	Acidic Solution	Basic Solution
+6	$Cr_2O_7^{-2}$ (orange)	CrO_4^{-2} (yellow)
+3	$Cr(H_2O)_6^{+3}$ (violet)	$Cr(H_2O)_2(OH)_4^{-}$ (green)
0	Cr metal	

Hydrogen peroxide is a suitable oxidizing agent in a basic solution. Since H_2O_2 is a weak acid the HO_2^- ion or the peroxide ion, O_2^{-2}, are ionic species formed in a basic solution.

Oxidation Number of Oxygen	Molecular or Ionic Species Present	
	Acidic Solution	Basic Solution
0	O_2	O_2
−1	H_2O_2	O_2^{-2} or HO_2^{-}
−2	H_2O	OH^{-}

The $E°$ values for the half reactions in basic solution are

$$4OH^- + Cr(OH)_4^{-}* \rightleftarrows CrO_4^{-2} + 4H_2O + 3e^-$$
$$+0.13 \text{ volt}$$
$$3OH^- \rightleftarrows HO_2^- + H_2O + 2e^-$$
$$-0.88 \text{ volt}$$

Before you proceed with the preparation, balance the equations for the reactions involved so you can calculate the number of moles of reactants required for each of the steps in the preparation. Record these in your laboratory notebook before coming to the laboratory.

Step 1. Conversion of $Cr(H_2O)_6^{+3}$
   to $Cr(H_2O)_2(OH)_4^{-}$ with an excess of strong base.
Step 2. Oxidation of $Cr(H_2O)_2(OH)_4^{-}$
   to CrO_4^{-2} by peroxide ion in a basic solution.
Step 3. Conversion of CrO_4^{-2}
   to $Cr_2O_7^{-2}$ by acidification with H_2SO_4.

---

*$Cr(OH)_4^{-}$ is a simplified formula for the ion $Cr(H_2O)_2(OH)_4^{-}$ without the water of hydration.

PROCEDURE

a. Weigh out 0.01 mole of chromium(III) acetate (chromic acetate), $Cr(CH_3COO)_3 \cdot H_2O$ (247.2 g/mole). Dissolve it in about 20 ml of distilled water in a small beaker. Warm slightly to hasten dissolving.

b. Pour 25 ml of 6 M KOH solution into a 250 ml Erlenmeyer flask. Add the chromium(III) acetate solution slowly to the flask. Swirl the flask to mix the solutions and to make sure that any chromium(III) hydroxide formed will dissolve in the excess base present.

c. Refer to the equation you balanced for Step 2 and note the number of moles of hydrogen peroxide required to oxidize the 0.01 moles of chromium(III) ion. Calculate the volume of commercial hydrogen peroxide, 3% by weight, required to obtain this many moles. Add an excess of about three times the calculated volume of hydrogen peroxide solution, add 1 or 2 boiling chips, and heat the flask to boiling. If the solution does not become yellow in color after boiling for a minute or two, add about 10 ml more hydrogen peroxide solution and bring to a boil again. Repeat if necessary but avoid too large an excess of H_2O_2.

d. After the solution turns yellow boil it gently until its volume has been reduced to about 30 ml. Any excess hydrogen peroxide should be decomposed during the boiling.

e. Allow the solution to cool for a few minutes.

Acidify by adding glacial acetic acid, 18 M CH_3COOH, dropwise (medicine dropper) until the solution becomes orange in color. The color of the dichromate ion, $Cr_2O_7^{-2}$, in solution is orange. Add 1 ml of 18 M CH_3COOH in excess.

f. Heat the solution to boiling and evaporate the solution to a volume of about 25 ml. Cool the solution using an ice bath to crystallize the $K_2Cr_2O_7$.

g. Filter the solid and wash with two 5 ml portions of ethyl alcohol. Dry and weigh the crystals. Compare the quantity obtained with the theoretical amount expected, calculated from the equations.

QUESTIONS AND EXERCISES

1. Write the equations for the reactions involved in each of the steps used in the preparation of $K_2Cr_2O_7$. Show your calculations for the amount of H_2O_2 required and for the expected yield of $K_2Cr_2O_7$.

2. What ionic species were present in the final acidic solution before it was cooled? What equilibria are present?

3. Considering the following solubility data, would you expect your sample of $K_2Cr_2O_7$ to be relatively pure? Why?

Temperature ($°C$)	Solubility in g/100 g water	
	KCH_3COO	$K_2Cr_2O_7$
0	217	5
20	256	12
40	323	26
60	350	43
80	380	61
100	—	80

4. Compare the $E°$ values of the half reactions for the oxidation of Cr(III) to Cr(VI) in a basic solution with that for the oxidation in an acidic solution. See the introductory section of this experiment for the former value and Appendix 8 for the latter value. Which oxidation is potentially the more spontaneous?

5. Note the half-reaction for the oxidation of H_2O_2 for which the $E°$ value is -0.68 volt (Appendix 8). Can you now suggest a reason for decomposing the excess H_2O_2 in Step d before the solution was acidified to convert CrO_4^{-2} to $Cr_2O_7^{-2}$?

6. Is the conversion of chromate ion to dichromate ion an oxidation reaction? Explain.

41

THE PREPARATION OF CHROME ALUM

In the previous experiment you prepared potassium dichromate from chromium(III) acetate by oxidation in a basic solution. In this experiment you'll reverse the process and reduce potassium dichromate with sulfur dioxide in an acidic solution to produce a chromium(III) salt called chrome alum. Study the chart listing various oxidation numbers for chromium given in Experiment 40 and note the changes in color and ionic species which will be involved. Recall also from Experiment 39 that chrome alum, $KCr(SO_4)_2 \cdot 12 H_2O$ is a double salt resulting from the crystallization of the ionic species $Cr(H_2O)_6^{+3}$, $K(H_2O)_6^+$, and SO_4^{-2} within the same crystal lattice.

Refer to Appendix 8 for the $E°$ values for the half-reaction involving the reduction of Cr(VI) to Cr(III) and the half-reaction for the oxidation of SO_2 to SO_4^{-2}, both in acid solution. Before coming to the laboratory, balance the equation for this oxidation-reduction reaction and record it in your laboratory notebook.

PROCEDURE

a. Weigh out 0.05 mole of $K_2Cr_2O_7$ (294.2 g/mole) and add it to 60 ml of 3 M H_2SO_4. Warm to dissolve the $K_2Cr_2O_7$. Set aside to cool to room temperature.

b. Set up the sulfur dioxide generator shown in Fig. 41-1. Clamp the flask on an iron ring over a wire screen so that a burner may be used to heat the flask if necessary.

How many moles of SO_2 are required to reduce 0.05 mole of $K_2Cr_2O_7$? See the equation you balanced previously. How many moles of $Na_2S_2O_5$ should be used to produce this SO_2 by reaction with 6 M H_2SO_4? Convert the number of moles to grams of $Na_2S_2O_5$ and use about double this amount in the generator.

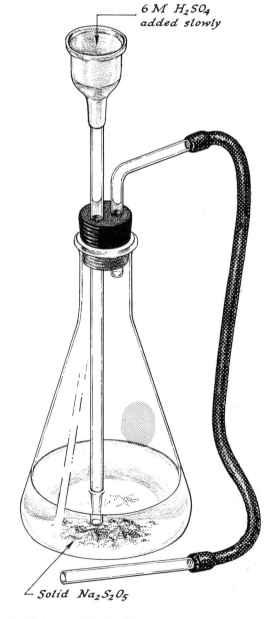

6 M H_2SO_4 added slowly

Solid $Na_2S_2O_5$

Fig. 41-1. A sulphur dioxide generator.

c. Add about 50 ml of tap water to the solid $Na_2S_2O_5$ in the generator. Attach a 10 cm piece of glass tubing to the hose leading from the generator and place it in the 125 ml Erlenmeyer flask.

d. Cool the $K_2Cr_2O_7$ solution to about 25°C before starting to generate the SO_2. **Caution:** Use an ice bath when necessary to maintain the $K_2Cr_2O_7$ solution below 40°C during the reduction of the dichromate. This is necessary to prevent complicating side reactions. Use a fume hood if available.

e. Add 10 ml portions of 6 M H_2SO_4 very slowly to the generator as needed to produce a steady flow of SO_2 gas. Warm the generator with a small flame from time to time as necessary.

f. Allow the reaction to continue until the solution turns from orange to a dark blue-green color. Stir or swirl the solution periodically, watching the temperature carefully. To check the color of the solution, place a drop on a filter paper and note the circle of color produced as the solution diffuses. The reduction is complete when no orange color is noted before the spot dries. (Estimated time for reaction is about 30 minutes.)

g. Pour the solution into an evaporating dish. Cover loosely and allow it to stand until crystals of chrome alum have formed. If the crystallization is allowed to proceed slowly, over a period of several days, larger crystals will be formed. Filter and allow to dry.

h. Weigh the dry crystals and calculate the percent yield you obtained.

QUESTIONS AND EXERCISES

1. Write the equations for the reactions involved in the experiment as requested in the introduction. Include the reaction for the production of sulfur dioxide.

2. Under what conditions could you grow large crystals of chrome alum?

3. Examine one of the larger crystals you prepared. Note any outstanding features of its geometric symmetry and prepare a sketch showing these.

4. What are the building blocks of the chrome alum crystal? Draw a three-dimensional structural formula for each of the ionic species involved.

5. Show calculations of the amounts of reactants required and the theoretical yield expected.

LIGHTING AND ADJUSTING A GAS BURNER

Two commonly used laboratory gas burners are illustrated in Fig. A1-1. They are similar in working principle, but differ in appearance and in adjustment and control.

To light a gas burner, hold a lighted match a little to one side and above the barrel of the burner. Turn on the main gas supply. If your burner is equipped with a gas adjustment, as is the one on the left in Fig. A1-1, turn the main gas supply (gas cock) on full and control the gas flow, using the burner gas control. If the burner is not equipped with a gas control, adjust the gas flow using the gas cock.

Adjust the amount of air needed as indicated in Fig. A1-2. A yellow smoky flame needs more air. Reduce the gas flow if the flame rises off the

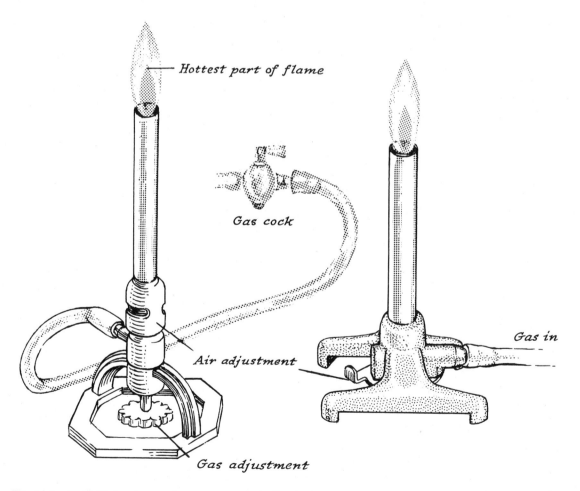

Fig. A1-1. **Typical laboratory gas burners**—*parts and adjustments.*

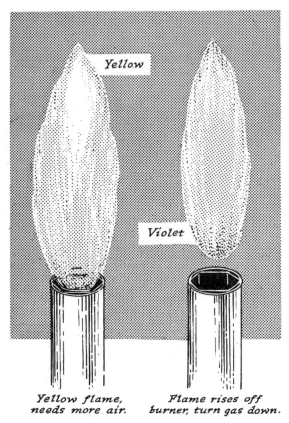

Fig. A1-2. **Flames resulting** *from improper gas–air*
adjustment.

burner. If the flame "strikes back," or burns inside the barrel near the air adjustment, turn the gas off for a moment. *Do not touch the hot barrel.* Allow the burner to cool, reduce the air intake, and relight the burner.

When you have some extra time try the experiment shown in Fig. A1-3. Suspend a wooden match in the barrel of the unlighted burner. Light the burner. What can you conclude about this zone of the flame from this experiment?

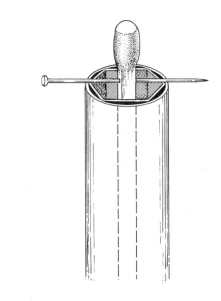

Fig. A1-3. **Investigation of one zone of the burner flame.**

WORKING WITH GLASS

HOW TO CUT, FIRE-POLISH, AND BEND GLASS TUBING

Hold the glass tubing firmly between the thumb and an edge of a triangular file as shown in Fig. A2-1. Rotate the glass about one-fourth of a turn to make a short, sharp scratch on the glass tubing.

Place your thumbs together, opposite the scratch; pull and bend quickly to snap the glass tubing at the mark.

To fire-polish the freshly cut edges, hold one end of the glass tubing in the hottest part of the burner flame and rotate the tube back and forth until the edges are rounded. Do not fire-polish so long that the end of the tube begins to close. **Caution:** Hot glass looks like cool glass. Put the hot glass on a wire gauze to cool, then fire-polish the other end of the tubing.

Heat the glass tubing in a burner flame, in the position shown in Fig. A2-2, rotating the glass in the hottest part of the flame. Allow the tubing to become slightly shorter as the glass melts and the walls thicken to about twice their original thickness. After the glass becomes quite soft and thickened, remove it from the flame and pull the tubing until the desired diameter (jet tip) is obtained. Place the hot glass on a wire gauze to cool. Cut the glass in the middle of the drawn-out portion and fire-polish the sharp ends.

Heat the glass tubing by rotating it back and forth in a flat burner flame, using a wing top as shown in Fig. A2-3. Continue heating the tubing until the glass becomes quite soft and is just beginning to sag as it is rotated. Remove the tubing from the burner flame and bend it by raising the ends to obtain the desired angle. Since hot glass tends to sag, bending it in this manner will produce a more uniformly smooth bend. Fig. A2-3 also contrasts the difference between a "good" bend (upper bend) and two "bad" bends. The middle bend resulted from holding the glass too low in the flame so that the middle

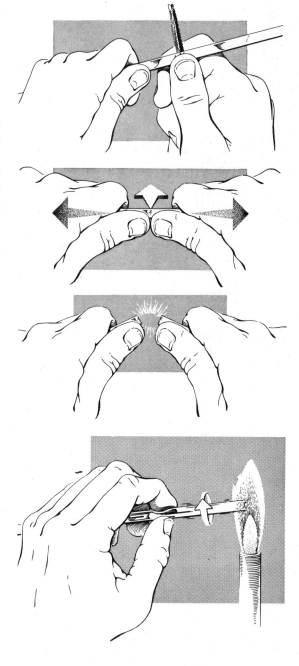

Fig. A2-1. **Cutting and fire-polishing** *glass tubing.*

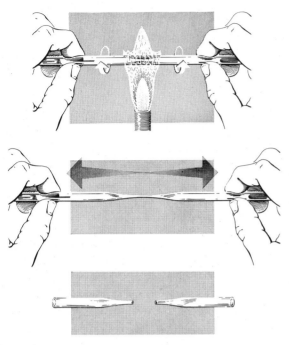

Fig. A2-2. **Drawing glass tubing** *to form a jet tip.*

of the tubing was in the cool portion of the flame. The bottom bend was produced by concentrating the flame on too narrow a portion of the glass tubing, which frequently results when a wing top is not used to spread the flame.

INSERTING GLASS TUBING OR A THERMOMETER INTO A RUBBER STOPPER

Before attempting to insert glass tubing into a rubber stopper be sure that the hole in the stopper is large enough that it will stretch easily to accommodate the tubing. A drop of glycerine or some water placed in the hole of the stopper or on the tip of the glass will serve as a lubricant.

Protect your hands by wrapping the glass with a piece of cloth or towel. Hold the glass near the stopper and push it with a gentle twisting motion. Do not force excessively as you insert glass tubing or a thermometer. **Be very careful.** If you experience any difficulty, consult your teacher.

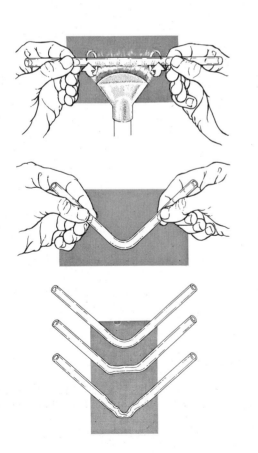

Fig. A2-3. **Making a smooth** $90°$ **bend in glass tubing.**

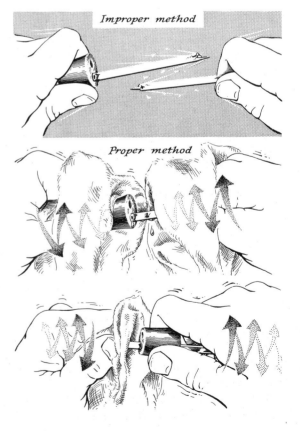

Fig. A2-4. **Inserting glass tubing** *into a stopper.*

MEASUREMENT—THE METRIC SYSTEM

LENGTH

A rectangular metal block is measured and found to have the following dimensions:

length = 12.1 cm,
width = 9.8 cm,
depth = 6.4 cm.

EXERCISES

1. Add two times the length to two times the width to obtain the perimeter of the largest face. Express your answer to nearest 0.1 cm. (*Answer:* 43.8 cm.)

2. Find the area of the largest face. (*Answer:* 119 cm².)

3. Find the volume of the block. (*Answer:* 760 cm³.)

   If the block had been measured in English units, its dimensions would have been recorded as:

   length = $4\frac{3}{4}$ inches,
   width = $3\frac{7}{8}$ inches,
   depth = $2\frac{1}{2}$ inches.

4. Find the perimeter and the area of the largest face using these measurements expressed in the English system. (*Answer:* Perimeter = $17\frac{1}{4}$ inches; area = $18\frac{13}{32}$ inches².)

5. Find the volume of the block using English units. (*Answer:* Volume = $46\frac{1}{64}$ inches³.)

6. Did you find the metric or the English units easier to use?

Although the English units can be expressed as decimals, conversions are required when using ordinary "rulers." The metric system is the common system used in most countries throughout the world and is used by all scientists. In this course, all measurements will be expressed in the metric system.

In the metric system the meter is the fundamental unit of length. One meter is equal to 100 cm. One centimeter is *almost* $\frac{1}{2}$ inch. There are 2.54 cm per inch. One thousand meters equal 1 *kilo*meter.

WEIGHT (Actually Mass)

The weight of the metal block is found to be 2.100 kg (2100 g) or 4 lb and 10 oz. A gram is a small unit of mass. A five cent piece weighs about 5 g. There are about 454 g to a pound. Since the gram is such a small unit, a larger unit is defined: 1 *kilo*gram is equal to 1000 g.

VOLUME

You are familiar with such measures of volume in the English system as pint, quart, and gallon. In the metric system, the fundamental unit of volume is the liter. A liter is a little larger than a quart. A liter is defined as the volume of 1 kg of water at 4°C. Since a liter is a rather large unit, it is divided into one thousand sub-units called *milliliters*. A milliliter is very nearly the volume of a cube 1 cm on each edge (actually, 1 ml = 1.000028 cm³).

DENSITY

The density (D) of a solid is defined as the mass per unit of volume and has the dimensions in the English system of pounds per cubic inch or pounds per cubic foot. In the metric system it is generally expressed in grams per cubic centimeter for solids and liquids, and grams per liter for gases.

EXERCISE

Calculate the density of the block of metal using the weight given above and the volume calculated above.

$$D = \frac{\text{mass}}{\text{volume}}$$ (*Answer:* D = 2.8 g/cm³)

SUMMARY OF METRIC UNITS
USED IN THIS COURSE

Note: *kilo* = 1000; *centi* = 0.01; *milli* = 0.001

Fundamental Units	Conversion Factors
Weight: gram (g) (actually mass)	1 *kilo*gram (kg) = 1000 g
	1 *centi*gram (cg) = 0.01 g
	1 *milli*gram (mg) = 0.001 g
Length: meter (m)	1 *kilo*meter (km) = 1000 m
	1 *centi*meter (cm) = 0.01 m
	1 *milli*meter (mm) = 0.001 m
Volume: liter (l)	1 *milli*liter (ml) = 0.001 liter
	1 ml = 1.000028 (cm³)

ADDITIONAL EXERCISES

1. Change:

   (a) 454 g to kilograms
   (b) 3.2 kg to grams to milligrams
   (c) 13 mm to centimeters to meters
   (d) 760 mm to centimeters to meters
   (e) 4.1 m to centimeters to millimeters
   (f) 1500 ml to liters
   (g) 250 ml to liters
   (h) 1.3 liters to milliliters

2. Calculate the weight of 323 cm³ of water at 4.0°C.

3. If 17 g of ammonia gas occupy a volume of 22.4 liters, calculate the density of the gas.

4

EXPERIMENTAL ERRORS

There is some degree of uncertainty in every measurement. We usually try to distinguish between two contributions to uncertainty: limitations of accuracy, and limitations of precision.

Accuracy expresses how closely the measurement comes to the true or accepted value. A measurement may be extremely reproducible, giving the same results each time, yet it may not actually measure that which it is supposed to measure. In such a case, the accuracy of a result may be very uncertain. Finding the source of inaccuracy requires making the same determination by several other methods. It is therefore not easy to specify the accuracy of a measurement.

Precision or reproducibility expresses the variation found when experiments are performed in which the same procedure is used repeatedly. Any measurement has some uncertainty resulting from limitations of the measuring device and the experimenter's ability to use the device. The following chart shows typical uncertainty values associated with the quality of apparatus generally used in this course. This does not include gross errors due to blunders or lack of knowledge of proper procedures for making observations.

UNCERTAINTIES ASSOCIATED WITH
MEASUREMENTS MADE USING
VARIOUS INSTRUMENTS

Instruments	Typical Uncertainty
Triple-beam (centigram) balance	± 0.01 g
Platform balance	± 0.5 g
50 ml graduated cylinder	± 0.2 ml
10 ml graduated cylinder	± 0.1 ml
$-10°C$ to $110°C$ thermometer	$\pm 0.2°C$
50 ml buret	± 0.02 ml
50 ml gas measuring tube	± 0.02 ml

In recording data it is an important step to estimate and record the uncertainty. For example, if you weigh a piece of copper wire on a triple-beam balance, you might record

Weight of copper wire: 2.89 g $\pm$ 0.01 g

The significance of "± 0.01 g" is that a repetition of the measurement is expected to give one of the results, 2.88, 2.89, or 2.90. If many repetitions of the measurement are made, the central value, 2.89, is expected to occur more often than the values 2.88 or 2.90, or more extreme values.

Another way to express the uncertainty is to indicate its magnitude as a percentage of the measured quantity. For the example given above, the percentage uncertainty is

$$\frac{0.01 \text{ g}}{2.89 \text{ g}} \times 100 = 0.35\%$$

So the measurement could be recorded as

Weight of copper wire: 2.89 g $\pm$ 0.35%

This method has several advantages when we consider how errors affect calculated results, especially those which involve multiplication or division. It is also a clearer way to compare uncertainties in quantities of different magnitude. For example, a much larger piece of copper might weigh 28.92 g ± 0.01 g. The percentage error is

$$\frac{0.01 \text{ g}}{28.92 \text{ g}} \times 100 = 0.035\%$$

This weight of copper would be recorded as

28.92 g $\pm$ 0.035%

If this latter piece of copper were weighed on a less sensitive device such as the platform balance, we might have found the weight to be 28.9 g $\pm$ 0.5 g or 28.9 g $\pm$ 1.7%, which is a much less precise value.

A third way of indicating the uncertainty is by the number of figures recorded. This is known as the method of "significant figures," and although it is often convenient it does not give as much information as the two preceding methods. In spite of its limitations, the method using significant figures is satisfactory for most purposes in this course.

In this method all digits that are certain and one additional uncertain digit are given. For example, for the copper wire weighed on the triple-beam balance we recorded 2.89 ± 0.01 g, so this weight would be written with three significant figures, 2.89. Note that the amount by which the last digit is uncertain is not specified when using only the significant figure notation 2.89. The numbers 2.89 ± 0.02 g, 2.89 ± 0.03 g or 2.89 ± 0.04 g would also be written as 2.89.

For the large piece of copper wire weighed on a platform balance we gave the value 28.9 g ± 0.5 g. This would be written as merely 28.9 g—three significant figures. Here again we are not sure how large the uncertainty is from the significant figure notation. The expression 28.9 ± 0.1 g indicates a greater precision than can be obtained from this balance. On the other hand, if you use 29 g with two significant figures, this could mean 29 ± 1 g, which is less than the precision of this balance.

THE USE OF SIGNIFICANT FIGURES IN RECORDING MEASUREMENTS

(1) The integers recorded are those that are certain and one more in which there is some uncertainty. Note the examples above.
(2) The number of significant figures has nothing to do with location of the decimal place. Thus, zeros that merely indicate the magnitude of the number are not significant figures.

For example, each of the numbers 36.09, 3.609, 0.3609, 0.003609 and 3609 has four significant figures. The number 36.090 has five significant figures, but what about the number 36090? In this case the last 0 may be a significant figure or it may merely mark the decimal place. To make it entirely clear that the last 0 is significant, the number should be written as 3.6090×10^4. If the 0 is not significant, 3.609×10^4 would indicate this.

Note again that using the number of significant figures to indicate uncertainty assumes that the uncertainty is always in the last place—it does not tell the degree of uncertainty.

THE PROPAGATION OF ERRORS IN CALCULATED RESULTS

So far we have discussed only the problems connected with recording a single measurement with the proper notation of uncertainty. Now we will consider how the uncertainties of several individual measurements carry over and combine when making various kinds of calculations to give us a derived result and its uncertainty.

A. Addition and Subtraction

When quantities are added or subtracted the maximum uncertainty in the result is the sum of the uncertainty for each of the component measurements.

EXAMPLE A. RESULT DERIVED BY SUBTRACTION

In Experiment 7 you obtained the weight of silver nitrate, $AgNO_3(s)$, by making two weighings such as these:

Weight of vial and $AgNO_3(s)$	15.34 g ± 0.01 g
Weight of vial	12.83 g ± 0.01 g
Weight of $AgNO_3(s)$	2.51 g ± 0.02 g

Note that the uncertainty in the derived result is ±0.02 g, or the sum of the individual uncertainties. Let us check this by using the values which will give the greatest and the least differences:

(15.34 + 0.01)	15.35 g	(15.34 − 0.01)	15.33 g
(12.83 − 0.01)	12.82 g	(12.83 + 0.01)	12.84 g
Difference	2.53 g		2.49 g

These numbers are in accord with the notation 2.51 g ± 0.02 g.

EXAMPLE B. RESULT DERIVED BY ADDITION

In Experiment 8 you weighed out a sample of sodium chloride, $NaCl(s)$, with an uncertainty of ±0.02 g. Later you added this weight to the weight of silver nitrate, $AgNO_3(s)$, also known with an uncertainty of ±0.02 g:

Weight of $NaCl(s)$	0.87 g ± 0.02 g
Weight of $AgNO_3(s)$	2.51 g ± 0.02 g
Sum	3.38 g ± 0.04 g

Note that the uncertainty in the derived result is ±0.04 g. Check this by finding the greatest and least values for the sum, as was done in Example A.

EXAMPLES USING THE SIGNIFICANT
FIGURE METHOD

In Example A, only three significant figures can
be used to express the difference, 2.51 g, since the
uncertainties involved occur in the hundredths
place. This means that the first two numbers are
known with certainty, but there is some question
about the last digit. Note that in subtraction
(or addition) you cannot use the actual number
of significant figures in the data (four in the
above example), but you must observe in which
position, tenths, hundredths, etc., the figure with
"doubt" occurs.

Consider a more extreme example. Add:

27   cm $\pm$ 1 cm   uncertainty in the units place
2.35 cm $\pm$ 0.001 cm   uncertainty in the hun-
                                      dredths place

The former value limits the answer to 29 cm $\pm$ 1
cm or to two significant figures, 29 cm.

Note that the method of using significant figures is superficially more simple but does not
always communicate the magnitude of the uncertainty. Nevertheless, it is adequate for most
of the calculations we shall make.

EXERCISES

Calculate the maximum uncertainty in each of the
following.

	Subtraction		Addition
1.	40.2 ± 0.2°C	2.	1500 ± 10 cm
	-10.2 ± 0.2°C		1500 ± 10 cm
			481 ± 1 cm
			$+ 481 \pm 1$ cm
3.	103.24 ± 0.01 g	4.	5.18 ± 0.02 g
	$- 98.13 \pm 0.01$ g		$+1.76 \pm 0.02$ g

5. How many significant figures are there in each of
the calculated quantities of Exercises 1–4?

B. Multiplication and Division

In multiplication and division the derived uncertainty is not simply the sum of the uncertainties
in the factors. It is the sum of the *percentage*
uncertainties in the factors.

EXAMPLE A

Calculate the heat, Q, as in Experiment 5, absorbed by 306 ± 2 g of water when its temperature changes by 20.0 ± 0.4°C.

Since it takes 1 calorie to raise the temperature
of 1 gram of water one degree centigrade, it takes
306 calories to heat 306 grams one degree and
306 ± 2 g $\times 20.0 \pm 0.4$°C calories to heat this
weight twenty degrees. Let us find the uncertainty in the calculated product by considering
the greatest value and the least value we could
obtain:

Greatest:

$$308 \text{ g} \times 20.4°\text{C} \times 1 \frac{\text{calorie}}{\text{g}°\text{C}} = 6283.2 \text{ calories}$$

Least:

$$304 \text{ g} \times 19.6°\text{C} \times 1 \frac{\text{calorie}}{\text{g}°\text{C}} = 5958.4 \text{ calories}$$

The average for these two products is 6120.8
$\pm$ 162.4 calories. This clearly indicates that the
uncertainty is located between 100 and 200 calories, and the answer should be written

$$Q = 6100 \pm 200 \text{ calories}$$

Expressing values as percentages, we find that

% uncertainty in 306

$$= \frac{2}{306} \times 100 = 0.65 = 0.7\%$$

% uncertainty in 20.0

$$= \frac{0.4}{20.0} \times 100 = 2.0\%$$

Total uncertainty in product $\overline{2.7\%}$

$306 \times 20.0 = 6120$ calories

$6120 \times 2.7\% = 160$, or rounded off,
                                    6100 ± 200 calories

When using significant figures we assume that
the product or quotient will assume the same
number of significant figures as the least precise
component. This is not an exact rule but is often
convenient to use. Each of the components in
this example has three significant figures (306 and
20.0); therefore, the answer is presumed to have
three. Thus, in the term 6120 the uncertainty is
considered to be in the tens place (the 2). We
should write this 6.12×10^3 to show that the last
0 is not significant. In this instance the use of
significant figures gives a misleading estimate of

the uncertainty. This is because we have assumed that the certainty of the result is determined entirely by the least precise component when in reality the uncertainty of each of the components contributes to the uncertainty of the product. We record only the number 6.12×10^3, whereas actually it is $6.12 \times 10^3 \pm 0.16$.

EXAMPLE B

Calculate the ratio of moles of aluminum to moles of silver if the moles of aluminum are 1.49 ± 0.02 and the moles of silver are 0.51 ± 0.02.

$$\frac{\text{moles of aluminum}}{\text{moles of silver}} = \frac{1.49 \pm 0.02}{0.51 \pm 0.02} = \frac{1.49 \pm 1.3\%}{0.51 \pm 3.9\%}$$

Answer: $2.92 \pm 5.2\%$ or 2.92 ± 0.15.

Using significant figures, we have

1.49 = three significant figures
0.51 = two significant figures

The answer should have two significant figures so 2.92 is rounded off to 2.9.

EXERCISES

6. Find the area of a rectangle measured to be 10.0 ± 0.1 cm by 2.5 ± 0.1 cm and calculate the uncertainty by each method (by using significant figures and by summing of percent uncertainty). Make a drawing of the rectangle, shading in the area of uncertainty. Calculate the area of the shaded part, and compare this to the calculated uncertainty.

7. Find the heat absorbed if 200 g ± 0.5 g of water is heated $5.0 \pm 0.2°C$.

8. Find the heat of combustion (calories per gram) for a substance if 9800 ± 200 calories are liberated when 1.23 ± 0.02 g of it burns. Express your answer to the correct number of significant figures. Uncertainty need not be reported.

9. Calculate the heat of solidification for the above substance if 210 ± 70 calories of heat are liberated as 10.3 ± 0.2 g of it solidifies. Express your answer to the correct number of significant figures.

ROUNDING OFF NUMBERS

Calculated results usually contain more digits than are justified from the uncertainty in the data. For example, find the area of a rectangle 15.2 cm

± 0.1 cm by 13.2 cm ± 0.1 cm. The product, neglecting uncertainty, is 200.64 cm². This is a more precise value than you would expect with an uncertainty of 0.1 cm in each measurement. By using the data giving the largest product, 15.3 cm $\times$ 13.3 cm $=$ 203.49 cm², and the smallest product, 15.1 cm $\times$ 13.1 cm $=$ 197.81 cm², it is obvious that the area should be expressed to only three significant figures. You therefore round off the 200.64 to the nearest digit in the units placed to obtain 201 cm².

Similarly, if the number 56.24 is to be rounded off to three digits, you would use 56.2 since 0.24 is nearer 0.2 than 0.3. Also:

> 234.57 rounded off to four digits is 234.6;
> 234.12 rounded off to four digits is 234.1;
> 234.546 rounded off to five digits is 234.55;
> 234.546 rounded off to four digits is 234.5.

When a 5 is dropped the last digit remaining is changed to the next higher even number if the digit is odd, and is left unchanged if the digit is even.

EXAMPLE: 234.75 is rounded off to 234.8; 234.45 is rounded off to 234.4

SUMMARY

1. Propagation of Uncertainty in Calculations

(A) *Addition and subtraction*
    The uncertainty is the sum of the uncertainties for each of the component quantities.
    For significant figure method: include all those figures in which there is no doubt and one in which there is some uncertainty.

(B) *Multiplication and division*
    The uncertainty is the sum of the *percentage* uncertainty for each of the component quantities.
    For significant figure method: include as many figures in the result as there are in the component with the least number of significant figures.

2. Accuracy of a Result

(A) It is usually difficult to estimate uncertainty associated with accuracy. If different methods have been used to measure the same quantity, the variation among the results is a clue to accuracy. Of course, if the true or an acceptable value is known, you may calculate the percentage error as well as the uncertainty in the calculation as based on the precision of the measurements.

The inaccuracy is usually expressed as

$$\% \text{ error} = \frac{\text{difference between experimental and accepted value}}{\text{accepted value}} \times 100$$

(B) In cases where the true or acceptable value is not known and also when you have a number of determinations of the same value, you may calculate the deviation from the average. There are several ways of indicating a central tendency.

(1) You may express the average deviation from the average value. See Exercise 1-4 in the text.

(2) You may indicate the range within which a certain percentage of cases falls. In more rigorous statistical analysis you may calculate what is known as the standard deviation. Approximately two-thirds of the cases of a normal distribution fall within a ± 1 standard deviation. It is therefore customary to give the range within which about 67% of the cases occur.

APPENDIX **5**

SOME MATHEMATICS USEFUL IN CHEMISTRY

EXPONENTIAL NUMBERS

Expressing Numbers in Exponential Notation

In chemistry we often have to deal with either very large numbers, such as 602,300,000,000,000,-000,000,000, the number of molecules in a mole, or very small numbers, such as 0.000 000 000 000 000 000 000 000 000 911 g, the mass of an electron. Such numbers are much more conveniently expressed as some number between 1 and 10 times 10 raised to a power. For example:

$$1 = 1 \times 10^0 \qquad 1 = \frac{1}{10^0} = 1$$

$$10 = 1 \times 10^1 \qquad 0.1 = \frac{1}{10^1} = 1 \times 10^{-1}$$

$$100 = 1 \times 10^2 \qquad 0.01 = \frac{1}{10^2} = 1 \times 10^{-2}$$

$$1000 = 1 \times 10^3 \qquad 0.001 = \frac{1}{10^3} = 1 \times 10^{-3}$$

Thus

$$602,300,000,000,000,000,000,000 = 6.023 \times 10^{23}$$

and

0.000 000 000 000 000 000 000 000 000 911

$$= 9.11 \times 10^{-28}$$

Writing a number in this form is a "shorthand" method of expression. The notation 6.023×10^{23} tells us to multiply 6.023 by 10 twenty-three times. The notation 9.11×10^{-28} tells us to divide 9.11 by 10 twenty-eight times. Recall that to multiply by 10 moves the decimal point one place to the right and to divide by 10 moves the decimal point one place to the left.

This method of notation is extremely useful in indicating the number of significant figures in a measurement and eliminates the confusion that sometimes occurs as to whether or not zeros in a number are significant.

EXAMPLES

(a) The value given above for the number of molecules in a mole is known to be reliable to four significant figures. It is therefore written in exponential form as 6.023×10^{23} molecules. The number 6.023 expresses the proper number of significant figures. The term 10^{23} indicates the magnitude of the term.

(b) The numbers below are correctly written using exponential notation.

$$186,000 \pm 1,000 = 1.86 \times 10^5$$

(three significant figures)

$$0.00430 \pm 0.00001 = 4.30 \times 10^{-3}$$

(three significant figures)

$$10002 \pm 1 = 1.0002 \times 10^4 \quad \text{(five significant figures)}$$

EXERCISES

1. Express each of the following in exponential notation. (Each should consist of the product of a *number* between 1 and 10 which reflects the number of significant figures and a *power of ten. Examples:* $22,400 \pm 100 = 2.24 \times 10^4$; $0.0056 \pm 0.0001 = 5.6 \times 10^{-3}$.)

(a) 300 ± 100 (f) 0.0000094 ± 0.0000001

(b) $85,000 \pm 1000$ (g) 0.000183 ± 0.000001

(c) $186,251 \pm 1$ (h) 0.0155 ± 0.0001

(d) $16,100,000 \pm 100,000$ (i) 0.0080 ± 0.0001

(e) 0.005 ± 0.001 (j) 80.10 ± 0.01

2. Change each of the following back to its non-exponential form. (*Examples:* $2.24 \times 10^4 = 22,400 \pm 100$; $4.30 \times 10^{-3} = 0.00430 \pm 0.00001$.)

(a) 3×10^2 (f) 9.4×10^{-6}

(b) 8.5×10^4 (g) 1.83×10^{-4}

(c) 1.86251×10^5 (h) 1.55×10^{-2}

(d) 1.61×10^7 (i) 8.010×10^1

(e) 5×10^{-3} (j) 8.0×10^{-3}

3. Change the following powers of ten as indicated.
Examples:
$224 \times 10^5 = 2.24 \times 10^?$
Answer:
$224 \times 10^5 = 2.24 \times 10^7$.
$3224 \times 10^{-5} = 3.224 \times 10^?$
Answer:
$3224 \times 10^{-5} = 3.224 \times 10^{-2}$.

(a) $448 \times 10^4 = 4.48 \times 10^?$

(b) $0.035 \times 10^8 = 3.5 \times 10^?$

(c) $2.35 \times 10^4 = \underline{\hspace{1cm}} \times 10^5$

(d) $8.1 \times 10^6 = \underline{\hspace{1cm}} \times 10^4$

(e) $324.5 \times 10^9 = \underline{\hspace{1cm}} \times 10^{11}$

(f) $224 \times 10^{-5} = 2.24 \times 10^?$

(g) $0.045 \times 10^{-9} = 4.5 \times 10^?$

(h) $76.16 \times 10^{-4} = 7616 \times 10^{-2}$ (put the decimal point in the proper place)

(i) $3.1 \times 10^{-6} = \underline{\hspace{1cm}} \times 10^{-3}$

(j) $5.423 \times 10^{-9} = \underline{\hspace{1cm}} \times 10^{-11}$

Addition and Subtraction of Exponential Quantities

To add or subtract exponential numbers, first express them to the same power of 10, then add or subtract them.

EXAMPLES

(a) $2.3 \times 10^4 + 1.4 \times 10^5$
$$= 2.3 \times 10^4 + 14 \times 10^4 = 16 \times 10^4$$

(b) $9.6 \times 10^5 - 3.2 \times 10^4$
$$= 9.6 \times 10^5 - 0.32 \times 10^5 = 9.3 \times 10^5$$

EXERCISES

1. $2.3 \times 10^4 + 4.6 \times 10^4 =$

2. $2.3 \times 10^4 + 5.3 \times 10^5 =$

3. $8.6 \times 10^{-3} + 5.0 \times 10^{-4} = 9.1 \times 10^{-3}$ (*answer*)

4. $2.18 \times 10^{-2} - 1.09 \times 10^{-2} =$

5. $6.23 \times 10^{-9} - 8.5 \times 10^{-10} =$

6. $8.6 \times 10^7 - 3.0 \times 10^6 = 8.3 \times 10^7$ (*answer*)

Multiplication and Division of Exponential Quantities

To multiply numbers written in exponential form, add the exponents, providing they are expressed to the same base (commonly powers of ten), and multiply the other factors.

EXAMPLES

(a) $10^1 \times 10^2 \times 10^4 = 10^{1+2+4} = 10^7$

(b) $10^{-2} \times 10^3 \times 10^5 = 10^{-2+3+5} = 10^6$

(c) $(1.0 \times 10^2) (2.2 \times 10^3) (1.5 \times 10^4)$
$$= 1.0 \times 2.2 \times 1.5 \times 10^{2+3+4} = 3.3 \times 10^9$$

EXERCISES

(*Express your answer in standard exponential notation*)

1. $10^2 \times 10^3 =$

2. $(2 \times 10^7) (2 \times 10^4) =$

3. $(1.2 \times 10^{12}) (8.0 \times 10^8) =$

4. $(2.5 \times 10^8) (4.0 \times 10^{-3}) =$

5. $(1.3 \times 10^{-6}) (3.0 \times 10^{-4}) =$

To divide exponential numbers, subtract the exponents, providing they are expressed to the same base, and divide the other factors.

EXAMPLES

(a) $10^4 \div 10^1 = 10^{4-1} = 10^3$

(b) $8 \times 10^3 \div 2 \times 10^3 = 8 \div 2 \times 10^{3-3} = 4 \times 10^0 = 4$

(c) $\dfrac{2 \times 10^3 \times 1 \times 10^{-2} \times 3 \times 10^6}{6 \times 10^{-6}}$
$$= \frac{2 \times 1 \times 3}{6} \times \frac{10^{3-2+6}}{10^{-6}} = \frac{10^7}{10^{-6}} = 10^{7-(-6)} = 10^{13}$$

EXERCISES

1. $10^6 \div 10^2 = 10^?$

2. $2.7 \times 10^8 \div 3 \times 10^5 =$

3. $4.5 \times 10^{-9} \div 5 \times 10^4 =$

4. $1.77 \times 10^8 \div 3 \times 10^{-3} =$

5. $1.45 \times 10^{-8} \div 5.0 \times 10^{-12} =$

Square Root of Exponential Quantities

To take the square root of an exponential number, multiply the exponent by $\frac{1}{2}$ and obtain the square root of the other factor. If the exponent is not divisible evenly by two, change the non-exponential factor by moving the decimal point to the right or to the left, whichever is most convenient, and make the required change in the exponent.

EXAMPLES

(a) $\sqrt{y^4} = (y^4)^{\frac{1}{2}} = y^2$

(b) $(4 \times 10^2)^{\frac{1}{2}} = 4^{\frac{1}{2}} \times (10^2)^{\frac{1}{2}} = 2 \times 10 = 20$

(c) $(9 \times 10^4)^{\frac{1}{2}} = 9^{\frac{1}{2}} \times (10^4)^{\frac{1}{2}} = 3 \times 10^2 = 300$

(d) $(2.5 \times 10^5)^{\frac{1}{2}} = (25 \times 10^4)^{\frac{1}{2}}$
$$= 25^{\frac{1}{2}} \times (10^4)^{\frac{1}{2}} = 5 \times 10^2$$

(e) $(10 \times 10^9)^{\frac{1}{2}} = (1.0 \times 10^{10})^{\frac{1}{2}}$
$$= 1.0^{\frac{1}{2}} \times (10^{10})^{\frac{1}{2}} = 1 \times 10^5$$

EXERCISES

(*Express your answers in correct exponential notation*)

1. $\sqrt{10^8} =$

2. $(2.5 \times 10^7)^{\frac{1}{2}} =$

3. $(62.5 \times 10^{-5})^{\frac{1}{2}} =$

4. $\sqrt{16} \times 10^{12} =$

5. $(16.9 \times 10^{11})^{\frac{1}{2}} =$

GRAPHING RELATIONSHIPS

Many factors are found to be interdependent. As the temperature of a gas increases, the volume increases if other conditions are not changing. Such a relationship in which two values change in the same direction (one remains larger than the other by the same factor) is a **direct relationship**. A direct relationship may be expressed mathematically as $x = ky$ or $x/y = k$, where k is a constant. Consider the following example of the direct relationship between the volume of a gas, V, and its absolute temperature, T, where $V = kT$. Note the straight line which results when the values are plotted. See Fig. A5-1.

Volume (liters)	Temperature (°K)
1	120
2	240
3	360

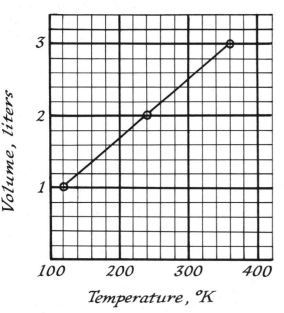

Fig. A5-1. **Graph for** $V = kT$.

EXAMPLES

(a) If $k = 1$, we find that $x = y$. As x increases in value y also increases. Plotting these values on a graph with values of x along the horizontal axis (abscissa) and y along the vertical axis (ordinate) we obtain Fig. A5-2.

x	y
1	1
3	3
5	5

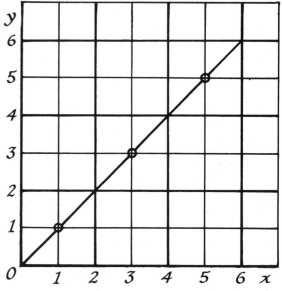

Fig. A5-2. **Graph for** $x = y$.

(b) If $k = 2$, we find that $x = 2y$. Plotting these values, we obtain Fig. A5-3.

x	y
2	1
4	2
6	3

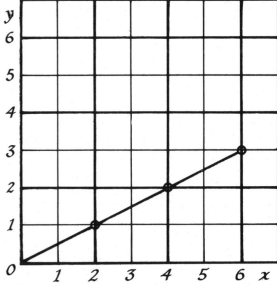

Fig. A5-3. **Graph for** $x = 2y$.

Note that in either case the plot is a straight line passing through the origin where $x = y = 0$.

When one value becomes larger by a given factor and the other becomes smaller by the same factor, we have an **inverse relationship,** which is expressed mathematically as $xy = k$ or $y = k/x$.

If $k = 6$, we find these values for x and y. Plotting these values we obtain Fig. A5-4.

EXAMPLE

x	y
1	6
2	3
3	2
6	1

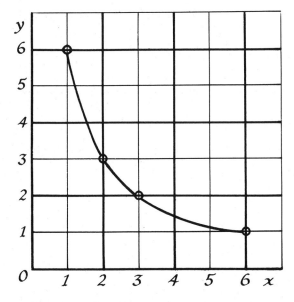

Fig. A5-4. **Graph for** $xy = 6$.

The relationship of gas pressure and volume discussed in Chapter 1 of the Textbook is an example of an inverse relationship in which $P = k/V$ or $PV = k$. Note the type of curve which results when the data for the pressure and volume of 32.0 grams of oxygen gas is plotted in Fig. A5-5.

Pressure (atmospheres)	Volume (liters)
0.100	224
0.200	109
0.400	57.5
0.600	38.0
0.800	27.7
1.00	22.4

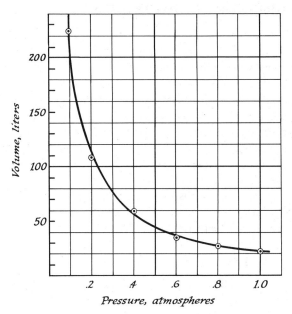

Fig. A5-5. **Graph for** $PV = k$.

Note that in an inverse relationship, for any value of k (except $k = 0$), when x becomes very large, y becomes very small and approaches but never reaches zero. When y becomes very large, x becomes very small but never reaches zero.

EXERCISES

1. Plot four values of x and y in which the ratio is direct and $k = 3$.

2. Plot six values of x and y in which the ratio is inverse and $k = 3$. Start with $x = 1$ and $y = 3$.

3. What is the value for k in the following:

$x = .2$	$y = .4$
$x = .6$	$y = 1.2$
$x = 1.8$	$y = 3.6$

Plot these values.

4. The volume of a partially inflated rubber balloon varies inversely with the external pressure.

   (a) Write an equation to describe this relationship. Use P for pressure and V for volume.

   (b) It is found experimentally that when the pressure is 1 atmosphere the balloon has a volume of 22.4 liters. When the pressure is increased to 2 atmospheres the volume decreases to 11.2 liters. What is the value of k in the equation?

   (c) What would the volume be under a pressure of 12 atmospheres? Of $\frac{1}{2}$ atmosphere?

ADDING, SUBTRACTING, MULTI-PLYING, AND DIVIDING EQUATIONS

Many of the fundamentals you have learned in algebra are extremely useful in chemistry. Some of the more commonly used manipulations are briefly reviewed here. Study each example as a means of refreshing your previous experience.

Let us consider two pairs of equations. The first pair you will recognize from your experience in algebra, while the second pair makes use of symbols common to chemistry. They are otherwise identical.

(a) $2a + b = 2c$ (b) $2C + O_2 = 2CO$
    $2c + b = 2e$ $2CO + O_2 = 2CO_2$

When we add the equations we obtain

$$2a + 2b + 2c = 2c + 2e \qquad (A5.1)$$
$$2C + 2O_2 + 2CO = 2CO + 2CO_2 \quad (A5.2)$$

The same quantity may be added or subtracted from each side of an equation without changing the equality. Subtracting $2c$ from both sides of equation $(A5.1)$, we obtain

$$2a + 2b = 2e$$

Subtracting 2 CO from both sides of equation $(A5.2)$, we obtain

$$2C + 2O_2 = 2CO_2$$

Each side of an equation may be divided by the same quantity without changing the equality. Dividing by 2 we obtain

$$a + b = e$$

which is the sum of the two equations in example (a), and

$$C + O_2 = CO_2$$

which is the sum of the two equations in example (b).

Let us consider two more pairs of equations:

(a) $a + b = c + 26d$
    $e + b = c + 24d$

(b) $C(diamond) + O_2(g)* = CO_2(g) + 94.50$ kcal
    $C(graphite) + O_2(g) = CO_2(g) + 94.05$ kcal

Subtracting one equation from the other we obtain:

$$a - e = 2d \qquad (A5.3)$$

and

$$C(diamond) - C(graphite) = 0.45 \text{ kcal} \quad (A5.4)$$

Adding e to both sides of equation $(A5.3)$ and $C(graphite)$ to both sides of equation $(A5.4)$, we obtain:

$$a = e + 2d$$

and

$$C(diamond) = C(graphite) + 0.45 \text{ kcal}$$

EXERCISES

1. Given the following two steps for the production of SO_3, add these equations to get the equation for the production of SO_3 from S and O_2.

$$S(s)* + O_2(g) = SO_2(g)$$
$$SO_2(g) + \tfrac{1}{2} O_2(g) = SO_3(g)$$

2. Add the following two reactions so that e^- cancels out.

$$Zn(s) = Zn^{+2}(aq)* + 2 e^-$$
$$e^- + Ag^+(aq) = Ag(s)$$

3. Energy is required to evaporate water. The following equations indicate the energy released when hydrogen and oxygen are burned to form water. Find the energy required to evaporate $H_2O(l)$.* [*Hint:* _____kcal $+ H_2O(l) = H_2O(g)$.]

$$H_2(g) + \tfrac{1}{2} O_2(g) = H_2O(g) + 57.80 \text{ kcal}$$
$$H_2(g) + \tfrac{1}{2} O_2(g) = H_2O(l) + 68.32 \text{ kcal}$$

$*g =$ gas; $s =$ solid; $l =$ liquid; $aq =$ aqueous.

OPTIONAL EXPERIMENTS

4a (OPTIONAL)

FURTHER INVESTIGATIONS OF A BURNING CANDLE

As you investigated the burning candle, no doubt many unanswered questions came to mind. Perhaps there are other questions for which you have been able to find satisfactory answers. The purpose of this experiment is to help you to find clues that will enable you to postulate answers to some of the unanswered questions. As you perform the experiments outlined below, keep thinking about possible answers to the following questions:

Why is the flame blue at the base, dark in the center, and yellow elsewhere?

What is the purpose of the wick in a candle?

Why is it possible to extinguish a candle flame by blowing on it?

Why is the flame shaped as it is?

PROCEDURE

a. Using a clothespin for a clamp, hold a piece of glass tubing about 8 cm long and 8 mm diameter in the flame of a burning candle so that one end of the tubing is well within the inner dark part of the flame. After holding the tubing steadily in this position for a few seconds, hold a lighted match to its outside end. (See Fig. 4a-1.) Record your observations.

b. Hold the same piece of glass tubing in the upper bright part of the flame and again hold a lighted match to its outside end. Record your observations.

c. Light a candle and allow it to burn for about half a minute. With a lighted match in hand, quickly blow out the candle and hold the match about an inch from the wick in the column of "smoke" emanating from the wick. See Fig. 4a-2. Record your observations.

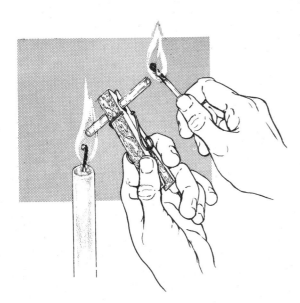

Fig. 4a-1. **Investigating** *the dark zone of flame.*

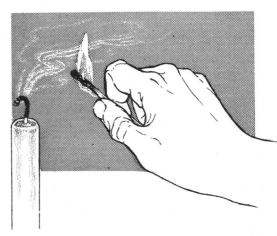

Fig. 4a-2. **Investigating the vapors.**

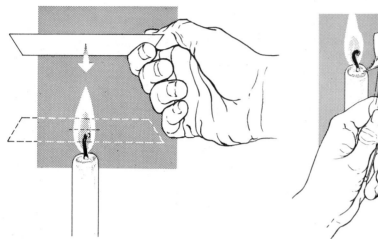

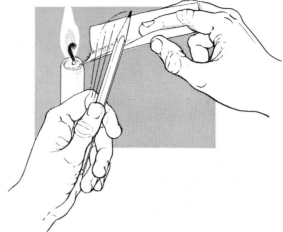

Fig. 4a-3.   **Zones in the flame.**

Fig. 4a-5.   **Investigating** *the liquid in the bowl of a candle.*

d. Move a horizontally held piece of white cardboard quickly down over the flame of a burning candle to the position shown in Fig. 4a-3. Hold the cardboard in this position just long enough for the flame to scorch through to the upper side of the cardboard but not long enough to cause it to burst into flame. Note the pattern of the scorched area.

e. Try lighting some candle wax without a wick. Try lighting wick material such as a piece of string without candle material. Try several different materials as wick materials by sticking them into the side of your candle (as shown in Fig. 4a-4): a toothpick, a paper matchstick, a piece of yarn, braided picture

wire, a piece of copper wire, a piece of string. Try your best to make each "wick" function properly. What are some of the necessary properties for wick materials?

f. Scrape some "soot" from the piece of glass tubing used earlier into the liquid in the bowl of a burning candle. Observe the motion of these particles in the liquid. (See Fig. 4a-5.)

g. Wind a length of copper wire (16 gauge or heavier) around a pencil about ten times, leaving enough uncoiled to serve as a handle. Slip the coiled wire off the pencil and lower it into the candle flame as shown in Fig. 4a-6. Record your observations.

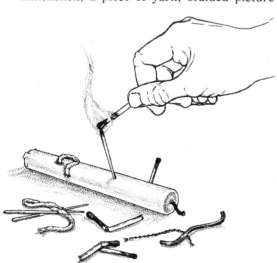

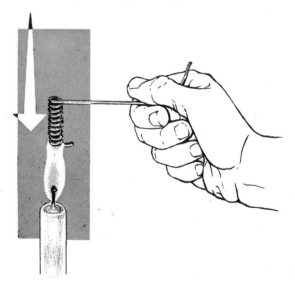

Fig. 4a-4.   **The nature of wicks.**

Fig. 4a-6.   **Lowering a copper coil** *into the flame.*

h. Snuff out the candle flame by wetting your thumb and forefinger and quickly pinching the burning wick. Relight the candle and try blowing the flame out by using different breath velocities.

i. Slide a horizontally held piece of slotted aluminum foil around the wick just below the base of the flame and above the melted wax as shown in Fig. 4a-7. Leave the aluminum in place for about 30 seconds. Account for the observed results.

j. Using a medicine dropper, place 1 or 2 drops of water on the molten wax in the bowl of the lighted candle. What happens?

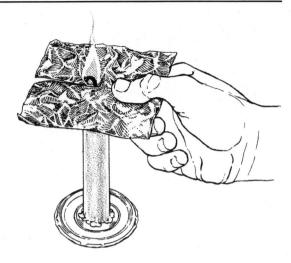

Fig. 4a-7. **Inserting an aluminum foil** *below the flame.*

QUESTIONS AND EXERCISES

1. Will a candle of larger diameter produce a larger flame? How can you construct a candle so that it will produce a larger flame? Test your hypothesis by experiment.

2. List as many of the necessary properties of a good wick material as you can.

3. Write a paragraph describing *what you think* is taking place within the candle flame. Justify your arguments with experimental evidence. Propose "answers" to as many of the introductory questions as you can.

A Question to Wonder About

How is the solid wax, which is composed of carbon and hydrogen, transformed into the products of combustion?

8a (OPTIONAL)

MASS RELATIONSHIPS ACCOMPANYING CHEMICAL CHANGES II

In this experiment you will use many of the techniques learned in previous experiments. If you encounter any difficulties with the various operations—weighing, decanting, filtering, or drying— refer to the figures in Experiments 7 and 8. The goal of this experiment is similar to that of Experiment 8.

PROCEDURE

a. Weigh a clean, dry beaker (100 or 250 ml) to the nearest 0.01 g.

b. Using the technique described in Fig. 8-1, p. 22, and Fig. 8a-1, weigh exactly 0.0050 *moles* of potassium chromate, K_2CrO_4, and transfer it to the weighed beaker.

c. Weigh a clean, dry Erlenmeyer flask (125 or 250 ml) to the nearest 0.01 g.

d. Weigh exactly 0.0050 *moles* of lead nitrate, $Pb(NO_3)_2$, as described in Fig. 8a-1 and transfer it to the weighed flask.

e. Dissolve each of the solids in about 25 ml of distilled water. Warm the solutions if desired to increase the rate of dissolving.

f. Add about 1 ml of the lead nitrate solution from the flask to the potassium chromate solution in the beaker and stir about one minute. Avoid splashing.

g. Add the rest of the lead nitrate, a few milliliters at a time, with stirring. Rinse out the last traces of lead nitrate with some distilled water, using a wash bottle. *Use as little water as is practical.* Several small volume rinses are more effective than a single one of larger volume. Heat for about five minutes, but do not let the solution boil vigorously. Allow the precipitate to settle.

h. Weigh a piece of filter paper and place it in a funnel for filtering, as in Figs. 8-4 and 8-5. Put the flask under the funnel and decant the clear liquid from the beaker into the funnel. Retain as much of the precipitate as possible in the beaker.

i. Wash the precipitate in the beaker by adding about 20 ml of distilled water and warming the mixture again. Let the precipitate settle and decant the liquid into the funnel, leaving as much of the precipitate as possible in the beaker. Wash the precipitate in the beaker with another 15 ml of distilled water.

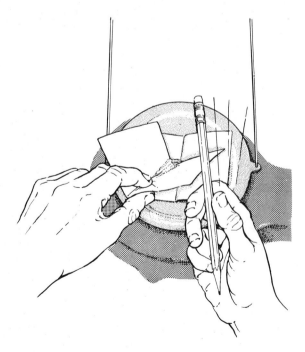

Fig. 8a-1. **Transferring** *the desired amount.*

j. Again decant the wash water into the filter paper in the funnel. Wash the sides of the beaker with 10 ml of distilled water and pour this also into the filter paper. It is not necessary to attempt to transfer all of the precipitate since you will later place the filter paper and its contents in the beaker to be dried.

k. When the filtering is complete, remove the flask and begin to evaporate the filtrate over a very low burner flame. Your teacher may suggest an alternate method to evaporate the solution to obtain the dry crystals overnight.

l. Remove the filter paper from the funnel. Unfold it to expose as much of the precipitate as possible to the air and place it loosely into the beaker. Dry the precipitate overnight as directed by your teacher.

m. When the residue in the flask is dry, weigh it in the flask.

n. When the precipitate in the beaker is dry, weigh the precipitate, the filter paper, and the beaker.

Data Table

Prepare a concise table for recording the measurements and observations made in this experiment.

CALCULATIONS

1. Determine the weight of each product.

2. Compare the sum of the weights of reactants with the sum of the weights of products. Are your results what you expected them to be? Justify your answer.

3. How many moles of each of the reactants were used and how many moles of each product were produced?

4. Write the formulas for the two reactants on the left of an arrow sign and the formulas for the two products on the right of the same arrow. Put the word *(solid)* after each formula to indicate the solid state condition of the original and of the final substances. There are other changes that have occurred during the reaction about which you will learn later.

Below each substance write the number of moles you used or formed.

Utilizing the number of moles involved, balance the equation.

5. Are your data consistent with the idea that atoms are conserved in a chemical reaction?

8b (OPTIONAL)

THE FORMULA OF A HYDRATE

Many salts which have been crystallized from a water solution appear to be perfectly dry, yet when heated yield large quantities of water. The crystals change form, even color sometimes, as the water is driven off, indicating that the water was present as an integral part of the crystal structure. Such compounds are called hydrates. The number of moles of water present per mole of anhydrous salt is usually some simple number.

In this experiment you will be given an appropriate hydrate selected by your teacher and you will find the weight of water driven off by heating, and the amount of anhydrous salt which remains. Your teacher will give you the weight of 1 mole of the anhydrous salt so you can find the empirical formula of the hydrate.

PROCEDURE

a. Organize a neat data sheet to record data and calculations. Place a clean dry crucible with cover in a triangle mounted on an iron ring. Heat with a nonluminous flame for two or three minutes.

b. When the crucible is cool enough for you to touch, transfer the crucible and cover to a balance and weigh them to the nearest 0.01 g.

c. Put enough of the hydrate crystals in the crucible to fill it one-fourth to one-third full. Replace the cover and weigh again.

d. Place the covered crucible on the triangle and heat gently until most of the water has been driven off, then increase the heat until the crucible bottom is at most a dull red. Maintain this temperature for five minutes. Allow the covered crucible to cool (in a desiccator if available).

e. When the crucible is cool enough to touch, transfer it and the cover to the balance and weigh them.

f. To make sure all the water is driven off, heat the crucible and cover to dull redness again. Cool and weigh. If your results do not agree within 0.02 g, consult your instructor concerning further heating and weighing.

Your data should include the following information:

Weight of crucible and cover

Weight of crucible, cover, and hydrate

Weight of crucible, cover, and anhydrous salt after first heating

Weight of crucible, cover, and anhydrous salt after second heating

Weight of 1 mole of anhydrous salt (from teacher)

CALCULATIONS

Calculate the number of moles of the anhydrous salt you prepared. How many moles of water were associated with 1 mole of anhydrous salt? Write the empirical formula for the hydrate.

QUESTIONS

1. Suggest reasons for weighing the crucible and anhydrous salt each time just as soon as it has cooled, not before or later.

2. Do your results agree exactly with those for a definite hydrate? If not, what are some plausible explanations for the deviation?

3. Can you suggest reasons why the above method might not be suitable for all hydrates?

14a (OPTIONAL)

A STUDY OF REACTION RATES II

In this experiment we shall continue our study of the factors which influence the rate of a reaction by investigating the rate of decomposition of aqueous sodium hypochlorite, NaOCl(*aq*). We shall use a commercially available bleaching solution which contains about 5% by weight sodium hypochlorite as a source of the hypochlorite ions, OCl⁻, which decompose according to the following equation:

$$2OCl^-(aq) \longrightarrow O_2(g) + 2Cl^-(aq)$$

Since the rate of this reaction is extremely slow under normal conditions, we shall use a solid catalyst, an oxide of cobalt, to catalyze each of the reactions studied. The catalyst will be prepared right in the reaction vessel just as we wish to initiate the decomposition by allowing a few milliliters of a 0.17 *M* solution of cobalt nitrate, $Co(NO_3)_2$, to react with some of the bleaching solution. The reaction for the formation of the solid catalyst is thought to be

$$2\,Co^{+2}(aq) + OCl^-(aq) + 2\,H_2O \longrightarrow Co_2O_3(s) + 4\,H^+(aq) + Cl^-(aq)$$

The rate of the hypochlorite decomposition will be followed by relating the volume of water displaced by the oxygen formed to the time intervals. The effect of temperature will be studied by determining the rate at room temperature and at approximately ten degrees above and below room temperature. The effect of concentration on the rate will be determined by diluting the bleaching solution.

Your teacher will designate which part or parts of the experiment will be done by you and your partner. One of the partners should prepare a data table for recording the time, every 30 seconds, and the volume of water displaced by the oxygen. Make an original and two copies. Before you write up the experiment you should exchange data with other partners so you will be able to plot the results of Parts I, II, III, and IV.

PROCEDURE

Set up the apparatus as shown in Fig. 14a-1. If the bent glass tubing is not available see Appendix 2 which describes how to cut, bend, and fire polish glass tubing. Also note the proper technique illustrated for inserting glass tubing through rubber stoppers. Your teacher may prefer to furnish you with pre-assembled stoppers and glass tubing. Use 125 ml Erlenmeyer flasks.

The apparatus will require less attention if the second flask is clamped to a ring stand.

Part I. Decomposition Rate at Room Temperature

a. Measure carefully 15.0 ml of the sodium hypochlorite solution into a graduated cylinder, determine its temperature, then pour it into the first Erlenmeyer flask. Place 3 ml of the cobalt nitrate solution into a 13 × 100 mm test tube and insert it carefully into the same Erlenmeyer flask as shown.

b. Fill the second Erlenmeyer flask full of water and replace the stopper.

c. Open the pinch clamp and fill the delivery tube leading to the 50 ml graduated cylinder by blowing into the rubber tubing which is attached to the short glass elbow inserted in the second Erlenmeyer flask. Close the pinch clamp while the tube is full of water.

d. Make all connections and check that the rubber stoppers fit tightly in the flasks. Remove the pinch clamp. If your apparatus is air tight only a few drops of water will drip into the graduated cylinder.

e. Note the time as you quickly tip the reaction

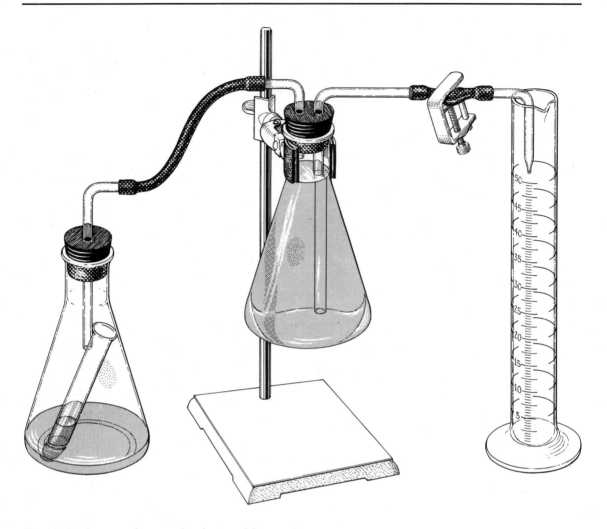

Fig. 14a-1. **Apparatus for measuring** *the rate of decomposition.*

flask slightly to pour the cobalt nitrate solution out of the test tube into the sodium hypochlorite solution.

f. Hold the erect flask at its neck and move it constantly with a *gentle* swinging motion to dislodge the gas bubbles from the solid catalyst in a uniform manner. This motion *must* be gentle and uniform in all trials.

g. Record the volume of water in the graduated cylinder every 30 seconds until about 50 ml has been collected.

Part II. Decomposition Rate Above Room Temperature

Rinse out the reaction flask and repeat the procedure as directed above except have the tem-

perature of the solutions in the reaction flask at about ten degrees centigrade above room temperature by warming in a lukewarm water bath.

Part III. Decomposition Rate Below Room Temperature

Repeat the procedure with the solutions in the reaction flask at about ten degrees centigrade below room temperature. Cool the flask and solutions in a cold water bath.

Part IV. Decomposition Rate Using a Two-fold Dilution of the Bleaching Solution

Repeat the procedure at room temperature as in Part I except add 18 ml of water to the sodium hypochlorite solution in the flask in order to effect a twofold dilution in the final volume.

Part V. Decomposition at Other Dilutions as Directed by Your Teacher

Part VI. Optional Extensions of This Experiment to be Assigned to Selected Students

a. Investigate various solid oxides as possible catalysts by using other solutions in place of the 0.17 M cobalt nitrate solution. For example, try 3 ml of 0.17 M ferric nitrate, $Fe(NO_3)_3$ solution and repeat the experiment.

b. Investigate combinations of solid oxide catalysts by using mixtures of solutions such as $Co(NO_3)_2$ and $Fe(NO_3)_3$ and precipitating mixed oxides as possible catalysts.

Organizing the Data

After exchanging data with other partners, plot the data from Parts I, II, III, and IV on the same graph. Plot the volume of oxygen produced along the ordinate and time along the abscissa. Label each run.

QUESTIONS

1. Make as quantitative a statement as possible concerning the relation between the temperature and the rate of the reaction.

2. If you had carried out the decomposition at 60°C, what would you predict the appearance of the curve to be?

3. Compare the observed rates for diluted and non-diluted NaOCl solutions.

4. Predict where the rate curve would be if the concentration of sodium hypochlorite in the bleaching solution were 10% instead of 5% present in the commercial bleach.

5. (*Optional*) Do other solid oxides serve as catalyst? What was the effect that you noted for a mixture of oxides?

29a (OPTIONAL)

THE PREPARATION OF SOME POLYMERS

Polymerization involves the chemical combination of a number of identical or similar molecules to form a complex molecule of high molecular weight. The small units may be combined by *condensation* polymerization or *addition* polymerization.

Condensation polymers are produced by reactions during which some simple molecule, such as water, is eliminated between functional groups, such as alcoholic —OH or acidic —COOH groups. In order to form long-chain molecules, two or more of each of these groups must be present in each of the reacting units.

Addition polymers are formed by the reaction of the monomeric units without the elimination of atoms. The monomer is usually an unsaturated organic compound such as ethylene, $H_2C{=}CH_2$, which in the presence of an initiator will undergo an addition reaction to form a long chain molecule such as polyethylene.

In this experiment directions are given for the preparation of two polymers of the *condensation* type, a Glyptal resin and an amine-aldehyde polymer, and an *addition* type, a methyl methacrylate polymer.

PROCEDURE

Part I. The Preparation of a Glyptal Resin

The condensation of polyhydroxy alcohols and polybasic acids or anhydrides leads to polyesters known as alkyd resins. These are used in making modern paints and enamels. A common member of this type is Glyptal resin formed from

glycerol   *ortho*phthalic acid

a. Place 2 g of glycerol and 3 g of powdered phthalic anhydride into a 50 ml beaker or a small tin can. Mix with a glass stirring rod. Cover with a watch glass and heat gently over an electric hot plate (a low burner flame may be used but care should be used since the resin is flammable). Keep heating until large bubbles form and the mixture puffs up. Allow the resin formed to cool.

b. Remove the resin from the container and grind it in a mortar. Try to dissolve some of it in a solvent suggested by your teacher. Do not heat over an open flame. When you have obtained a solution of the resin, pour some of it out on a piece of wood or metal and let it dry. Note the nature of the residue. Suggest a practical use for this type of resin.

Part II. The Preparation of an Amine-Aldehyde Type Polymer

In 1909, L. Baekeland first demonstrated the possibilities of forming plastics with formaldehyde, HCHO, and substituted aromatics such as phenol, ⬡—OH, in the presence of acid or alkaline catalysts. Such polymers are called Bakelite plastics. The first stages in the condensation reaction between phenol and formaldehyde are shown below

In this preparation we shall use an aromatic amine called aniline, ⬡—NH_2, instead of phenol. Its reaction with formaldehyde is analogous to the phenol-formaldehyde condensation.

Measure 10 ml of 40% formaldehyde solution, called formalin, into one test tube and 10 ml of a saturated aqueous solution of aniline hydrochloride into another test tube. Pour the solutions into a 50 ml beaker or a small tin can, simultaneously, in order to mix them. Note whether the reaction is exothermic or endothermic. Examine the product and record its properties.

Part III. The Depolymerization of a Methyl Methacrylate Polymer and the Subsequent Polymerization of the Monomer

The methyl methacrylate polymers are the nearest approach to an organic glass so far developed and are marketed in the United States under the trade names Lucite and Plexiglas. The structure of the polymer has been given as

$$H\!\!-\!\!\left[\!CH_2\!-\!\underset{\underset{COOCH_3}{|}}{\overset{\overset{CH_3}{|}}{C}}\!-\!CH_2\!-\!\underset{\underset{COOCH_3}{|}}{\overset{\overset{CH_3}{|}}{C}}\!\right]_n\!\!-\!\!CH\!\!=\!\!\underset{\underset{COOCH_3}{|}}{\overset{\overset{CH_3}{|}}{C}}$$

By distilling the polymer it can be readily depolymerized to form the monomer-methyl methacrylate:

$$\underset{H}{\overset{H}{\diagdown}}C\!\!=\!\!C\underset{COOCH_3}{\overset{CH_3}{\diagup}}$$

With the aid of an appropriate catalyst this monomer can be repolymerized. **Caution:** Do not attempt this experiment without the appropriate equipment. Use suitable precautions to avoid inhaling the vapors of the monomer-methyl methacrylate.

a. Place 25 g of Lucite or Plexiglas pellets or chips in a 100 ml distilling flask with ground glass connections. Attach an efficient condenser (double surface type) and distill using a small luminous flame. Move the flame to and fro around the sides of the flask. When the polymer softens it will soon begin to undergo rapid depolymerization at about 300°C. Continue the distillation until only a small amount of residue remains. Redistill the liquid and collect the distillate between 100–110°C. The yield of methylmethacrylate should be about 20 g. If the monomer is not going to be used within a day, it should be stored under refrigeration.

b. To repolymerize the methyl methacrylate, place 10 ml of the liquid in a small expendable glass container (such as a baby food jar) and add 0.01 to 0.02 g of benzoyl peroxide, $C_6H_5\!-\!\underset{\underset{O}{\|}}{C}\!-\!O\!-\!O\!-\!\underset{\underset{O}{\|}}{C}\!-\!C_6H_5$, as the initiator.

Cover it with a piece of aluminum foil, tucked in around the edges and held in place by a rubber band. Place the jar in a hot water bath and keep the temperature just below boiling for about 30 minutes or until polymerization is complete.

Allow the polymer to cool and record a description of its properties in your notebook.

QUESTIONS AND EXERCISES

1. Write equations for the reactions involved in each preparation you performed, using structural formulas for the monomers and polymers involved.
2. Which of the preparations involve condensation reactions?
3. Which are addition reactions?
4. Nylon is a generic name for polymeric amides including those formed by the reaction of adipic acid, $HOOC\!-\!(CH_2)_4\!-\!COOH$ and 1, 6-diaminohexane, $H_2N\!-\!(CH_2)_6\!-\!NH_2$. Show how these polyfunctional molecules can condense and form a long-chain polymer.

RELATIVE STRENGTHS OF ACIDS

IN AQUEOUS SOLUTION AT ROOM TEMPERATURE

All ions are aquated

$$HB \rightleftharpoons H^+(aq) + B^-(aq) \qquad K_A = \frac{[H^+][B^-]}{[HB]}$$

ACID	STRENGTH	REACTION	K_A
perchloric acid	very strong	$HClO_4 \longrightarrow H^+ + ClO_4^-$	very large
hydriodic acid		$HI \longrightarrow H^+ + I^-$	very large
hydrobromic acid		$HBr \longrightarrow H^+ + Br^-$	very large
hydrochloric acid		$HCl \longrightarrow H^+ + Cl^-$	very large
nitric acid		$HNO_3 \longrightarrow H^+ + NO_3^-$	very large
sulfuric acid	very strong	$H_2SO_4 \longrightarrow H^+ + HSO_4^-$	large
oxalic acid		$HOOCCOOH \longrightarrow H^+ + HOOCCOO^-$	5.4×10^{-2}
sulfurous acid ($SO_2 + H_2O$)		$H_2SO_3 \longrightarrow H^+ + HSO_3^-$	1.7×10^{-2}
hydrogen sulfate ion	strong	$HSO_4^- \longrightarrow H^+ + SO_4^{-2}$	1.3×10^{-2}
phosphoric acid		$H_3PO_4 \longrightarrow H^+ + H_2PO_4^-$	7.1×10^{-3}
ferric ion		$Fe(H_2O)_6^{+3} \longrightarrow H^+ + Fe(H_2O)_5(OH)^{+2}$	6.0×10^{-3}
hydrogen telluride		$H_2Te \longrightarrow H^+ + HTe^-$	2.3×10^{-3}
hydrofluoric acid	weak	$HF \longrightarrow H^+ + F^-$	6.7×10^{-4}
nitrous acid		$HNO_2 \longrightarrow H^+ + NO_2^-$	5.1×10^{-4}
hydrogen selenide		$H_2Se \longrightarrow H^+ + HSe^-$	1.7×10^{-4}
chromic ion		$Cr(H_2O)_6^{+3} \longrightarrow H^+ + Cr(H_2O)_5(OH)^{+2}$	1.5×10^{-4}
benzoic acid		$C_6H_5COOH \longrightarrow H^+ + C_6H_5COO^-$	6.6×10^{-5}
hydrogen oxalate ion		$HOOCCOO^- \longrightarrow H^+ + OOCCOO^{-2}$	5.4×10^{-5}
acetic acid	weak	$CH_3COOH \longrightarrow H^+ + CH_3COO^-$	1.8×10^{-5}
aluminum ion		$Al(H_2O)_6^{+3} \longrightarrow H^+ + Al(H_2O)_5(OH)^{+2}$	1.4×10^{-5}
carbonic acid ($CO_2 + H_2O$)		$H_2CO_3 \longrightarrow H^+ + HCO_3^-$	4.4×10^{-7}
hydrogen sulfide		$H_2S \longrightarrow H^+ + HS^-$	1.0×10^{-7}
dihydrogen phosphate ion		$H_2PO_4^- \longrightarrow H^+ + HPO_4^{-2}$	6.3×10^{-8}
hydrogen sulfite ion		$HSO_3^- \longrightarrow H^+ + SO_3^{-2}$	6.2×10^{-8}
ammonium ion	weak	$NH_4^+ \longrightarrow H^+ + NH_3$	5.7×10^{-10}
hydrogen carbonate ion		$HCO_3^- \longrightarrow H^+ + CO_3^{-2}$	4.7×10^{-11}
hydrogen telluride ion		$HTe^- \longrightarrow H^+ + Te^{-2}$	1.0×10^{-11}
hydrogen peroxide	very weak	$H_2O_2 \longrightarrow H^+ + HO_2^-$	2.4×10^{-12}
monohydrogen phosphate ion		$HPO_4^{-2} \longrightarrow H^+ + PO_4^{-3}$	4.4×10^{-13}
hydrogen sulfide ion		$HS^- \longrightarrow H^+ + S^{-2}$	1.3×10^{-13}
water		$H_2O \longrightarrow H^+ + OH^- \quad [H^+][OH^-] =$	1.0×10^{-14}
hydroxide ion		$OH^- \longrightarrow H^+ + O^{-2}$	$<10^{-36}$
ammonia	very weak	$NH_3 \longrightarrow H^+ + NH_2^-$	very small

STANDARD OXIDATION POTENTIALS FOR HALF-REACTIONS

IONIC CONCENTRATIONS, 1 M IN WATER AT 25°C

All ions are aquated

	HALF-REACTION	$E°$ (volts)	
Very strong reducing agents	$Li \longrightarrow e^- + Li^+$	3.00	Very weak oxidizing agents
	$Rb \longrightarrow e^- + Rb^+$	2.92	
	$K \longrightarrow e^- + K^+$	2.92	
	$Cs \longrightarrow e^- + Cs^+$	2.92	
	$Ba \longrightarrow 2e^- + Ba^{+2}$	2.90	
	$Sr \longrightarrow 2e^- + Sr^{+2}$	2.89	
	$Ca \longrightarrow 2e^- + Ca^{+2}$	2.87	
	$Na \longrightarrow e^- + Na^+$	2.71	
	$Mg \longrightarrow 2e^- + Mg^{+2}$	2.37	
	$Al \longrightarrow 3e^- + Al^{+3}$	1.66	
	$Mn \longrightarrow 2e^- + Mn^{+2}$	1.18	
	$H_2(g) + 2OH^- \longrightarrow 2e^- + 2H_2O$	0.83	
	$Zn \longrightarrow 2e^- + Zn^{+2}$	0.76	
	$Cr \longrightarrow 3e^- + Cr^{+3}$	0.74	
	$H_2Te \longrightarrow 2e^- + Te + 2H^+$	0.72	
	$2Ag + S^{-2} \longrightarrow 2e^- + Ag_2S$	0.69	
Reducing strength increases	$Fe \longrightarrow 2e^- + Fe^{+2}$	0.44	Oxidizing strength increases
	$H_2(g) \longrightarrow 2e^- + 2H^+ \ (10^{-7} \ M)$	0.414	
	$Cr^{+2} \longrightarrow e^- + Cr^{+3}$	0.41	
	$H_2Se \longrightarrow 2e^- + Se + 2H^+$	0.40	
	$Co \longrightarrow 2e^- + Co^{+2}$	0.28	
	$Ni \longrightarrow 2e^- + Ni^{+2}$	0.25	
	$Sn \longrightarrow 2e^- + Sn^{+2}$	0.14	
	$Pb \longrightarrow 2e^- + Pb^{+2}$	0.13	
	$H_2(g) \longrightarrow 2e^- + 2H^+$	0.00	
	$H_2S(g) \longrightarrow 2e^- + S + 2H^+$	−0.14	
	$Sn^{+2} \longrightarrow 2e^- + Sn^{+4}$	−0.15	
	$Cu^+ \longrightarrow e^- + Cu^{+2}$	−0.15	
	$SO_2(g) + 2H_2O \longrightarrow 2e^- + SO_4^{-2} + 4H^+$	−0.17	
	$Cu \longrightarrow 2e^- + Cu^{+2}$	−0.34	
	$Cu \longrightarrow e^- + Cu^+$	−0.52	
	$2I^- \longrightarrow 2e^- + I_2$	−0.53	
	$H_2O_2 \longrightarrow 2e^- + O_2(g) + 2H^+$	−0.68	
	$Fe^{+2} \longrightarrow e^- + Fe^{+3}$	−0.77	
	$NO_2(g) + H_2O \longrightarrow e^- + NO_3^- + 2H^+$	−0.78	
	$Hg(l) \longrightarrow 2e^- + Hg^{+2}$	−0.78	
	$Hg(l) \longrightarrow e^- + \frac{1}{2}Hg_2^{+2}$	−0.79	
	$Ag \longrightarrow e^- + Ag^+$	−0.80	
	$H_2O \longrightarrow 2e^- + \frac{1}{2}O_2(g) + 2H^+ \ (10^{-7} \ M)$	−0.815	
	$NO(g) + 2H_2O \longrightarrow 3e^- + NO_3^- + 4H^+$	−0.96	
	$Au + 4Cl^- \longrightarrow 3e^- + AuCl_4^-$	−1.00	
	$2Br^- \longrightarrow 2e^- + Br_2(l)$	−1.06	
	$H_2O \longrightarrow 2e^- + \frac{1}{2}O_2(g) + 2H^+$	−1.23	
	$Mn^{+2} + 2H_2O \longrightarrow 2e^- + MnO_2 + 4H^+$	−1.28	
	$2Cr^{+3} + 7H_2O \longrightarrow 6e^- + Cr_2O_7^{-2} + 14H^+$	−1.33	
	$2Cl^- \longrightarrow 2e^- + Cl_2(g)$	−1.36	
	$Au \longrightarrow 3e^- + Au^{+3}$	−1.50	
Very weak reducing agents	$Mn^{+2} + 4H_2O \longrightarrow 5e^- + MnO_4^- + 8H^+$	−1.52	Very strong oxidizing agents
	$2H_2O \longrightarrow 2e^- + H_2O_2 + 2H^+$	−1.77	
	$2F^- \longrightarrow 2e^- + F_2(g)$	−2.87	

APPENDIX 9

NAMES, FORMULAS, AND CHARGES
OF SOME COMMON IONS

POSITIVE IONS (CATIONS)		NEGATIVE IONS (ANIONS)	
aluminum	Al^{+3}	acetate	CH_3COO^-
ammonium	NH_4^+	bromide	Br^-
barium	Ba^{+2}	carbonate	CO_3^{-2}
calcium	Ca^{+2}	hydrogen carbonate ion, bicarbonate	HCO_3^-
chromium (II), chromous	Cr^{+2}	chlorate	ClO_3^-
chromium (III), chromic	Cr^{+3}	chloride	Cl^-
cobalt (II), cobaltous	Co^{+2}	chlorite	ClO_2^-
copper (I),* cuprous	Cu^+	chromate	CrO_4^{-2}
copper (II), cupric	Cu^{+2}	dichromate	$Cr_2O_7^{-2}$
hydrogen, hydronium	H^+, H_3O^+	fluoride	F^-
iron (II),* ferrous	Fe^{+2}	hydroxide	OH^-
iron (III), ferric	Fe^{+3}	hypochlorite	ClO^-
lead	Pb^{+2}	iodide	I^-
lithium	Li^+	nitrate	NO_3^-
magnesium	Mg^{+2}	nitrite	NO_2^-
manganese (II), manganous	Mn^{+2}	oxalate	$C_2O_4^{-2}$
mercury (I),* mercurous	Hg_2^{+2}	hydrogen oxalate ion, binoxalate	$HC_2O_4^-$
mercury (II), mercuric	Hg^{+2}	perchlorate	ClO_4^-
potassium	K^+	permanganate	MnO_4^-
silver	Ag^+	phosphate	PO_4^{-3}
strontium	Sr^{+2}	monohydrogen phosphate	HPO_4^{-2}
sodium	Na^+	dihydrogen phosphate	$H_2PO_4^-$
tin (II),* stannous	Sn^{+2}	sulfate	SO_4^{-2}
tin (IV), stannic	Sn^{+4}	hydrogen sulfate ion, bisulfate	HSO_4^-
zinc	Zn^{+2}	sulfide	S^{-2}
		hydrogen sulfide ion, bisulfide	HS^-
		sulfite	SO_3^{-2}
		hydrogen sulfite ion, bisulfite	HSO_3^-

* Aqueous solutions are readily oxidized by air.

Note: In ionic compounds the relative number of positive and negative ions is such that the sum of their electric charges is zero.

10

SOLUBILITY OF COMMON INORGANIC COMPOUNDS IN WATER

THESE IONS		FORM SOLUBLE COMPOUNDS (*Solubility greater than 0.1 M*)	FORM SLIGHTLY SOLUBLE COMPOUNDS (*Solubility less than 0.1 M*)
ANIONS		WITH THESE CATIONS	WITH THESE CATIONS
NO_3^-,	nitrate	Most cations	None
CH_3COO^-,	acetate	Most cations	Ag^+
Cl^-,	chloride	Most cations	$Ag^+, Pb^{+2}, Hg_2^{+2}, Cu^+$
Br^-,	bromide	Most cations	$Ag^+, Pb^{+2}, Hg_2^{+2}, Cu^+$
I^-,	iodide	Most cations	$Ag^+, Pb^{+2}, Hg_2^{+2}, Cu^+$
SO_4^{-2},	sulfate	Most cations	$Ba^{+2}, Sr^{+2}, Pb^{+2}, Ag^+, Ca^{+2}$
CrO_4^{-2},	chromate	Most cations	$Ba^{+2}, Sr^{+2}, Pb^{+2}, Ag^+$
S^{-2},	sulfide	NH_4^+, cations of Column 1, and cations of Column 2	Most other cations
OH^-,	hydroxide	NH_4^+, cations of Column 1 and Ba^{+2} and Sr^{+2} of Column 2	Most other cations
CO_3^{-2},	carbonate	NH_4^+ and cations of Column 1	Most other cations
PO_4^{-3},	phosphate	except Li^+	

	FORM SOLUBLE COMPOUNDS (*Solubility greater than 0.1 M*)	FORM SLIGHTLY SOLUBLE COMPOUNDS (*Solubility less than 0.1 M*)
CATIONS	WITH THESE ANIONS	WITH THESE ANIONS
Na^+, K^+, and other cations of Column 1 and NH_4^+	Most anions	No common anions
$H^+(aq)$	Most anions	No common anions

INTERNATIONAL ATOMIC WEIGHTS*

NAME	SYMBOL	ATOMIC NUMBER	ATOMIC WEIGHT	NAME	SYMBOL	ATOMIC NUMBER	ATOMIC WEIGHT
Actinium	Ac	89	(227)	Mercury	Hg	80	200.6
Aluminum	Al	13	27.0	Molybdenum	Mo	42	95.9
Americium	Am	95	(243)	Neodymium	Nd	60	144.2
Antimony	Sb	51	121.8	Neon	Ne	10	20.2
Argon	Ar	18	39.9	Neptunium	Np	93	(237)
Arsenic	As	33	74.9	Nickel	Ni	28	58.7
Astatine	At	85	(210)	Niobium	Nb	41	92.9
Barium	Ba	56	137.3	Nitrogen	N	7	14.01
Berkelium	Bk	97	245	Osmium	Os	76	190.2
Beryllium	Be	4	9.01	Oxygen	O	8	16.00
Bismuth	Bi	83	209.0	Palladium	Pd	46	106.4
Boron	B	5	10.8	Phosphorus	P	15	31.0
Bromine	Br	35	79.9	Platinum	Pt	78	195.1
Cadmium	Cd	48	112.4	Plutonium	Pu	94	(242)
Calcium	Ca	20	40.1	Polonium	Po	84	210
Californium	Cf	98	(251)	Potassium	K	19	39.1
Carbon	C	6	12.01	Praseodymium	Pr	59	140.9
Cerium	Ce	58	140.1	Promethium	Pm	61	(147)
Cesium	Cs	55	132.9	Protactinium	Pa	91	(231)
Chlorine	Cl	17	35.5	Radium	Ra	88	(226)
Chromium	Cr	24	52.0	Radon	Rn	86	(222)
Cobalt	Co	27	58.9	Rhenium	Re	75	186.2
Copper	Cu	29	63.5	Rhodium	Rh	45	102.9
Curium	Cm	96	(247)	Rubidium	Rb	37	85.5
Dysprosium	Dy	66	162.5	Ruthenium	Ru	44	101.1
Einsteinium	Es	99	(254)	Samarium	Sm	62	150.4
Erbium	Er	68	167.3	Scandium	Sc	21	45.0
Europium	Eu	63	152.0	Selenium	Se	34	79.0
Fermium	Fm	100	(253)	Silicon	Si	14	28.1
Fluorine	F	9	19.0	Silver	Ag	47	107.9
Francium	Fr	87	(223)	Sodium	Na	11	23.0
Gadolinium	Gd	64	157.3	Strontium	Sr	38	87.6
Gallium	Ga	31	69.7	Sulfur	S	16	32.1
Germanium	Ge	32	72.6	Tantalum	Ta	73	180.9
Gold	Au	79	197.0	Technetium	Tc	43	(99)
Hafnium	Hf	72	178.5	Tellurium	Te	52	127.6
Helium	He	2	4.00	Terbium	Tb	65	158.9
Holmium	Ho	67	164.9	Thallium	Tl	81	204.4
Hydrogen	H	1	1.008	Thorium	Th	90	232.0
Indium	In	49	114.8	Thulium	Tm	69	168.9
Iodine	I	53	126.9	Tin	Sn	50	118.7
Iridium	Ir	77	192.2	Titanium	Ti	22	47.9
Iron	Fe	26	55.8	Tungsten	W	74	183.9
Krypton	Kr	36	83.8	Uranium	U	92	238.0
Lanthanum	La	57	138.9	Vanadium	V	23	50.9
Lead	Pb	82	207.2	Xenon	Xe	54	131.3
Lithium	Li	3	6.94	Ytterbium	Yb	70	173.0
Lutetium	Lu	71	175.0	Yttrium	Y	39	88.9
Magnesium	Mg	12	24.3	Zinc	Zn	30	65.4
Manganese	Mn	25	54.9	Zirconium	Zr	40	91.2
Mendelevium	Md	101	(256)				

Parenthetical names refer to radioactive elements; the mass number (not the atomic weight) of the isotope with largest half-life is usually given.

*Latest values recommended by the International Union of Pure and Applied Chemistry, 1961.